A BOOK OF GOOD PLAYS

THE COPP CLARK LITERATURE SERIES

A Book
of
Good Plays

EDITED BY

Ronald J. McMaster

Ontario College of Education

THE COPP CLARK PUBLISHING CO. LIMITED

VANCOUVER   TORONTO   MONTREAL

[1231]

62

Preface

This collection of plays was made in response to numerous requests for a book that would promote understanding and appreciation of the one-act play and would encourage stage performances and some original dramatic writing. The plays were chosen from both conventional and experimental drama. They include comedy, tragedy, and fantasy and represent the work of some of the best known writers of the modern theatre.

Selection was not, of course, based on variety alone. Each play creates its own excitement and carries its own challenge. Each is a dramatic work of acknowledged appeal and recognized craftsmanship.

Stage diagrams, brief biographical sketches, a glossary of dramatic terms, and certain explanatory notes have been provided. For each play, I have offered some suggestions for dramatic production: those who attempt to perform the plays will receive the richest rewards for their efforts.

The questions, perhaps, warrant special mention. They have been graded A, B, and C to mark increasing difficulty so that they may be assigned in accordance with the needs of individual students. It is my hope that some of those marked C will provide our most gifted students with the intellectual and imaginative stimulation that they deserve.

I should like to thank those teachers who offered useful comments and valuable suggestions while the work was in progress. I should also like to thank Mr. Ronald Lane of The Copp Clark Publishing Co. Limited for his patience and his careful editing of the manuscript.

R. J. McM.

Acknowledgements

For permission to reprint copyrighted material, grateful acknowledgement is made to the following publishers:

Samuel French (Canada) Ltd., for "The Monkey's Paw," by W. W. Jacobs; "The Patchwork Quilt," by Rachel Lyman Field; and "Moon-Up," by Robert Arthur.

Coward-McCann, for "The Happy Journey," from *The Long Christmas Dinner*, by Thornton Wilder.

Longmans, Green & Co., Inc., for "The Valiant," by Holworthy Hall and Robert Middlemass.

Charles Scribner's Sons, for "The Old Lady Shows Her Medals," by James M. Barrie.

Cover Design by GRAHAM BYFIELD

Contents

Contents

THE ONE-ACT PLAY

BACKGROUND

The literary drama is one of the oldest of the fine arts. Aristotle called it "imitated human action." Although this definition is incomplete, it does stress the very important feature of representing life: drama is mainly an artistic treatment of life as the playwright sees it and feels it. This treatment may be read at home or viewed at the theatre. If read, it must be interpreted vividly and visualized as actually taking place. Primarily, though, it should be experienced as it is presented on stage before an audience that enjoys imaginative identification with the characters and their problems. Since drama seeks to present life, it contains action and conflict; the play progresses from a state of equilibrium to a climax and on to a feeling of satisfaction.

The complexity of drama is also worthy of note. It combines many arts and skills—literature, music, choreography, architecture, lighting, sound effects, costuming, make-up, and so on. Unlike other forms of literature that demand a satisfactory relationship between only the writer and the reader, a play demands a satisfactory relationship among the playwright, the director, the costumer, the lighting artist, the scene designer, the electrician, the stage carpenter, the prompter, the actors, and the audience. All these people contribute to the success of the total dramatic experience. Moreover, the wide variety of dramatic compositions—tragedy, comedy, melodrama, farce, historical play, "message" play, musical review, opera, fantasy—proves the intricacy of this literary form.

Just as the modern short story is an offspring of the novel, the modern one-act play is a child of the full-length drama. Both have inherited characteristics from their parents; yet, each has its own unique character. Just in relatively recent years has the one-act play achieved stature as an acceptable literary form. Although short plays had been popular as far back as Ancient Greek times, not until around 1890 did the one-act play reach a significant period of development. Prior to that time, one-act plays were used as curtain raisers in London theatres, for the purpose of delaying the important production of a full-length play until the late-dining audience arrived. Critics point to two causes for the change to the warm acceptance of short plays: The Repertory Theatre and The Little Theatre Movement. These groups popularized the one-act play by depending upon several of them for a single evening's entertainment. Perhaps an even more important cause for the great growth of the one-act play is the adoption of it by some of our finest writers—James Barrie, Bernard Shaw, John Masefield, John Galsworthy, Eugene O'Neill, and Thornton Wilder. Lastly, one must admit the potent influence of television on the one-act play: today, writers are constantly being encouraged to concentrate their efforts on this literary form because of the tremendous demand for new material that will fit into thirty-minute programming.

GENERAL CHARACTERISTICS

Although the technique of the one-act play is somewhat flexible, it does possess certain characteristics. Frequently it is compared to a short story. The comparison is good. In many respects, a one-act play is merely a short story in dramatic form. There is, however, one significant difference: in the play, the narrative on stage is presented solely through dialogue and action, while in a short story, direct author comment is often used. Other than this striking distinction, there are many similarities. Both the short story and the one-act play stress economy of means: no irrelevant action, information, nor characterization is allowed to detract from the impact of the unity of the whole. Both aim to produce a single impression, mood, or idea. Both require a single incident or, at most, a single plot usually covering a relatively short space of time: no sub-plots are permitted. Both display tension or conflict in some interesting way. Finally, both demand a sound plot structure that leads to a distinct climax.

PLOT

The plot of a one-act drama is essentially one of conflict or tension, although no violent struggle is necessary. In fact, sometimes in certain modern plays there is only a vague uneasiness experienced by the audience. Since there is time for only one plot to be advanced, a single incident often serves to clarify the conflict for the audience. This struggle may be mental (man against man), physical (man against nature), or moral (man against himself), and it must be suitable for dramatic presentation. For example, although a writer could create an exciting struggle between man and nature as he depicts the physical endurance of his hero combatting blizzards and fierce wolves, a playwright would have to abandon such a scheme because of the limitations of the stage. In addition, this single plot must seem plausible: a writer is not justified in concluding, for the sake of a happy ending, that the hero who has contracted an incurable disease is saved by a new miracle drug. Such a contrived dénouement is evidence of unsound plotting.

Good plotting requires competent handling of the stages of a one-act play: introduction, rising action, climax, and dénouement. In the introduction, we become acquainted with the main characters, the existing situation, and any preliminary exposition. The rising action starts with a complication that creates tension and often suspense as the main character becomes involved in some form of struggle or conflict. As this stage proceeds, crisis after crisis may be met until the emotional bomb, the climax, is presented. At this distinct point, we realize what the author considers the highest point of interest or emotion in his production. After the climax, the dénouement unfolds to clear up any unanswered question, to reveal the situation in which the characters now find themselves, and sometimes, to intimate their futures. In a good plot, the four stages are in correct proportion: brief introduction, detailed rising action, distinct climax, and short dénouement.

CHARACTERS

Only a few characters are presented in the one-act play, and their traits are revealed, not developed: there is no time for development. Because the play is short, often depicting one incident or situation, any unlikely change in a person's actions, beliefs, or qualities would seem contrived. The actions, reactions, and speeches must, therefore, be consistent with the character of the person as revealed. In actual life, the behaviour pattern of a murderer's becoming a social worker is possible; on stage, however, the change would seem incredible and ludicrous. The dramatist's concern is what seems real, not necessarily what is real.

In a one-act play, there is usually a predominant character, and it is through a sympathetic identification with this person and his problem that the audience enjoys an intense dramatic experience. His character may be revealed on stage in four main ways: by what he says, by what he does, by what others say of him, and by what others do in his presence.

SETTING

Most playwrights provide detailed stage directions and set descriptions. Remember, modern plays are meant to be read as well as acted, and therefore we often get a complete picture of place and time as background for the action. For example, read the following excerpt from Barrie's *The Old Lady Shows Her Medals*.

> A basement in a drab locality in London; the kitchen, sitting-room and bedroom of Mrs. Dowey, the charwoman. It is a poor room, as small as possible but clean and tidy; not at all bare, but containing many little articles and adornments.
>
> The door to the area is up left. The door to a small scullery is in the right wall rather up stage, below which is a small kitchen grate.
>
> In the left wall is a piece of furniture with the appearance of a cheap wardrobe, but which is, in fact, a bed which can be let down. Below this is a small chest of drawers.
>
> There is a shabby deal table, its length across the stage, set right centre, with two wooden chairs above it and one at each end.
>
> The time is about 5 p.m.

DIALOGUE

Good dialogue advances the plot, reveals character, and develops setting. While it performs these functions, it must seem natural, consistent, and interesting. No two characters should speak alike: by varying the choice of words, rhythm of speech, and sentence length the playwright creates individuals. Read aloud the following speeches taken from plays included in this book, and note how dramatically effective they are.

a) **Mrs. Willis.**   (*Trembling a little*) Emily—dead? Why, she couldn't be. She comes to see me real often—she's the only one of my children that does now—

b) **Announcer.** We interrupt our program to bring you an important bulletin! The hunt for Harry Holloway, who escaped last night from the State Penitentiary after serving five years of a fifteen year term for robbery and assault, has shifted to this locality. It is believed by State authorities that Holloway may be heading for his home on Big Pebbly River, in the hope of—

c) **Mrs. Tully.** I suppose I ought to know, me that has a son a prisoner in Germany. (*Rather bumptiously*) Being the only lady present that has that proud misfortune.

A FINAL WORD

In judging the worth of a one-act play, do not hold too rigidly to set standards. Remember that it is a comparatively new literary form, and only by experimentation through trial, error, and discovery will it grow to new heights. Judge it, then, by its power to entertain and enlighten. No finer criterion for evaluating literature exists!

SUGGESTED READING

ONE-ACT PLAYS

Barrie, J. M.	*Shall We Join the Ladies*
Brighouse, Harold	*The Price of Coal*
Chekhov, Anton	*The Boor*
Chekhov, Anton	*The Marriage Proposal*
Davey, Kathleen	*Unnatural Scene*
Denison, Merrill	*Brothers in Arms*
Dix, Beulah M.	*Allison's Lad*
Drinkwater, John	*X = 0*
Dunsany, Lord	*A Night at an Inn*
Ferguson, J. A.	*Campbell of Kilmhor*
Francis, J. O.	*The Poacher*
Galsworthy, John	*The Little Man*

GENERAL REFERENCE

Directing: *The Fundamentals of Play Directing*. Alexander Dean. Farrar, Straus and Cudahy, Inc.

Costuming: *A History of Costume*. Carl Kohler. George G. Harrap & Co. Ltd.

Make-up: *A Book of Make-Up*. Eric Ward. Samuel French.

Lighting: *Method of Lighting the Stage*. Stanley McCandless. Theatre Arts Inc.

Scenery: *Scenery for the Theatre*. Harold Burris-Meyer and Edward Cole. Little, Brown and Co.

General: *Here's How!* Herbert Hake. Row, Peterson & Company.
Producing the Play and The New Scene Technician's Handbook. John Gassner and Philip Barber. Dryden Press.
Theatre and School. Samuel Hume and L. M. Foster. Samuel French.
Writing the One-Act Play. Newcomb Hillebrand. Alfred A. Knopf, Inc.

The Monkey's Paw

A STORY IN THREE SCENES

by W. W. JACOBS

Dramatized by
Louis N. Parker

CHARACTERS

Mr. White

Mrs. White

Herbert

Sergeant-Major Morris

Mr. Sampson

THE MONKEY'S PAW

SCENE: *The living-room of an old-fashioned cottage on the outskirts of Fulham. Set corner-wise in the left angle at the back, a deep window; further front, left, three or four steps lead up to a door. Further forward, a dresser, with plates, glasses, etc. Right centre at back, an alcove, with the street door fully visible. On the inside of the street door, a wire letter-box. On the right, a cupboard, then a fireplace. In the centre, a round table. Against the wall, left back, an old-fashioned piano. A comfortable armchair each side of the fireplace. Other chairs. On the mantelpiece, a clock, old china figures, etc. An air of comfort pervades the room.*

I

(*At the rise of the curtain,* Mrs. White, *a pleasant-looking old woman, is seated in the armchair below the fire, attending to a kettle which is steaming on the fire, and keeping a laughing eye on* Mr. White *and* Herbert. *These two are seated at the right angle of the table nearest the fire with a chess-board between them.* Mr. White *is evidently losing. His hair is ruffled; his spectacles are high up on his forehead.* Herbert, *a fine young fellow, is looking with satisfaction at the move he has just made.* Mr. White *makes several attempts to move, but thinks better of them. There is a shaded lamp on the table. The door is tightly shut. The curtains of the window are drawn; but every now and then the wind is heard whistling outside.*)

Mr. White. (*Moving at last, and triumphant*) There, Herbert, my boy! Got you, I think.

3

Herbert. Oh, you're a deep 'un, dad, aren't you?

Mrs. White. Mean to say he's beaten you at last?

Herbert. Lor, no! Why, he's overlooked—

Mr. White. (*Very excited*) I see it! Lemme have that back!

Herbert. Not much. Rules of the game!

Mr. White. (*Disgusted*) I don't hold with them scientific rules. You turn what ought to be an innocent relaxation—

Mrs. White. Don't talk so much, father. You put him off—

Herbert. (*Laughing*) Not he!

Mr. White. (*Trying to distract his attention*) Hark at the wind.

Herbert. (*Drily*) Ah! I'm listening. Check.

Mr. White. (*Still trying to distract him*) I should hardly think Sergeant-Major Morris'd come to-night.

Herbert. Mate. (*Rises, goes up left*)

Mr. White. (*With an outbreak of disgust and sweeping the chessmen off the board*) That's the worst of living so far out. Your friends can't come for a quiet chat, and you addle your brains over a confounded—

Herbert. Now, father! Morris'll turn up all right.

Mr. White. (*Still in a temper*) Lovers' Lane, Fulham! Ho! of all the beastly, slushy, out-o'-the-way places to live in—! Pathway's a bog, and the road's a torrent. (*To Mrs. White, who has risen, and is at his side*) What's the County Council thinking of, that's what I want to know? Because this is the only house in the road it doesn't matter if nobody can get near it, I s'pose.

Mrs. White. Never mind, dear. Perhaps you'll win tomorrow. (*She moves to back of table.*)

Mr. White. Perhaps I'll—perhaps I'll—! What d'you mean? (*Bursts out laughing*) There! You always know what's going on inside o' me, don't you, mother?

Mrs. White. Ought to, after thirty years, John. (*She goes to dresser and busies herself wiping tumblers on tray there.*)

(*He rises, goes to fireplace, and lights pipe.*)

Herbert. (*Down centre*) And it's not such a bad place, dad, after all. One of the few old-fashioned houses left near London. None o' your stucco villas. Home-like, I call it. And so do you, or you wouldn't ha' bought it. (*Rolls a cigarette*)

Mr. White. (*Right, growling*) Nice job I made o' that, too! With two hundred pounds owin' on it.

Herbert. (*On back of chair, centre*) Why, I shall work that off in no time, dad. Matter o' three years, with the rise promised me.

Mr. White. If you don't get married.

Herbert. Not me. Not that sort.

Mrs. White. I wish you would, Herbert. A good, steady, lad—

(*She brings the tray with a bottle of whisky, glasses, a lemon, spoons, buns, and a knife to the table.*)

Herbert. Lots o' time, mother. Sufficient for the day—as the sayin' goes. Just now my dynamos don't leave me any time for love-making. Jealous they are, I tell you!

Mr. White. (*Chuckling*) I lay awake o' night often, and think: If Herbert took a nap, and let his what-d'you-call-ums—dynamos, run down, all Fulham would be in darkness. Lord! what a joke! (*Gets right centre*)

Herbert. Joke! And me with the sack! Pretty idea of a joke you've got, I don't think.

(Knock at outer door)

Mrs. White. Hark!

(Knock repeated, louder)

Mr. White. *(Going towards door)* That's him. That's the Sergeant-Major. *(He unlocks door, back.)*

Herbert. *(Removes chess-board)* Wonder what yarn he's got for us to-night. *(Places chess-board on piano)*

Mrs. White. *(Goes up right, busies herself putting the other armchair nearer fire, etc.)* Don't let the door slam, John.

(Mr. White opens the door a little, struggling with it. Wind; Sergeant-Major Morris, a veteran with a distinct military appearance—left arm gone—dressed as a commissionaire, is seen to enter. Mr. White helps him off with his coat, which he hangs up in the outer hall.)

Mr. White. *(At the door)* Slip in quick! It's as much as I can do to hold it against the wind.

Sergeant. Awful! Awful! *(Busy taking off his cloak, etc.)* And a mile up the road—by the cemetery—it's worse. Enough to blow the hair off your head.

Mr. White. Give me your stick.

Sergeant. If 'twasn't I knew what a welcome I'd get—

Mr. White. *(Preceding him into the room)* Sergeant-Major Morris!

Mrs. White. Tut! tut! So cold you must be! Come to the fire; do 'ee, now.

Sergeant. How are you, marm? *(To Herbert)* How's yourself, laddie? Not on duty yet, eh? Day week, eh?

Herbert. (*Centre*) No, sir. Night week. But there's half an hour yet.

Sergeant. (*Sitting in the armchair above the fire, which* Mrs. White *is motioning him towards*)

(Mr. White *mixes grog for* Morris.)

Thank'ee kindly, marm. That's good—hah! That's a sight better than the trenches at Chitral. That's better than settin' in a puddle with the rain pourin' down in buckets, and the natives takin' pot-shots at you.

Mrs. White. Didn't you have no umbrellas? (*Corner below fire, kneels before it, stirs it, etc.*)

Sergeant. Umbrell—? Ho! ho! That's good! Eh, White? That's good. Did ye hear what she said? Umbrellas!— *And* goloshes! *and* hot-water bottles!— Ho, yes! No offence, marm, but it's easy to see you was never a soldier.

Herbert. (*Rather hurt*) Mother spoke out o' kindness, sir.

Sergeant. And well I know it; and no offence intended. No, marm, 'ardship, 'ardship is the soldier's lot. Starvation, fever, and get yourself shot. That's a bit o' my own.

Mrs. White. You don't look to've taken much harm— except—(*Indicates his empty sleeve; she takes kettle to table, then returns to fire.*)

Sergeant. (*Showing a medal hidden under his coat*) And that I got this for. No, marm. Tough. Thomas Morris is tough. (Mr. White *is holding a glass of grog under the* Sergeant's *nose.*) And sober. What's this now?

Mr. White. Put your nose in it; you'll see.

Sergeant. Whisky? And hot? And sugar? And a slice o' lemon? No. I said I'd never—but seein' the sort o' night. Well! (*Waving the glass at them*) Here's another thousand a year!

Mr. White. (*Sits right of table, also with a glass*) Same to you, and many of 'em.

Sergeant. (*To* Herbert, *who has no glass*) What? Not you?

Herbert. (*Laughing and sitting across chair, centre*) Oh! 'tisn't for want of being sociable. But my work don't go with it. Not if 'twas ever so little. I've got to keep a cool head, a steady eye, and a still hand. The fly-wheel might gobble me up.

Mrs. White. Don't, Herbert. (*Sits in armchair below fire*)

Herbert. (*Laughing*) No fear, mother.

Sergeant. Ah! you electricians!—Sort o' magicians, you are. Light! says you—and light it is. And, power! says you—and the trams go whizzin'. And, knowledge! says you—and words go 'ummin' to the ends o' the world. It fair beats me—and I've seen a bit in my time, too.

Herbert. (*Nudges his father*) Your Indian magic? All a fake, governor. The fakir's fake.

Sergeant. Fake, you call it? I tell you, I've *seen* it.

Herbert. (*Nudging his father with his foot*) Oh, come, now! such as what? Come, now!

Sergeant. I've seen a cove with no more clothes on than a babby, (*To* Mrs. White) if you know what I mean— take an empty basket—empty, mind!—as empty as—as this here glass—

Mr. White. Hand it over, Morris. (*Hands it to* Herbert, *who goes quickly behind table and fills it*)

Sergeant. Which was not my intentions, but used for illustration.

Herbert. (*While mixing*) Oh, *I've* seen the basket trick; and I've read how it was done. Why, I could do it myself, with a bit o' practice. Ladle out something stronger.

(Herbert *brings him the glass.*)

Sergeant. Stronger?—what do you say to an old fakir chuckin' a rope up in the air—in the *air*, mind you!— and swarming up it, same as if it was 'ooked on—and vanishing clean out o'sight?—I've seen *that*.

(Herbert *goes to table, plunges a knife into a bun, and offers it to the* Sergeant *with exaggerated politeness.*)

Sergeant. (*Eyeing it with disgust*) Bun—? What for?
Herbert. That yarn takes it.

(Mr. *and* Mrs. White *delighted*)

Sergeant. Mean to say you doubt my word?
Mrs. White. No, no! He's only taking you off.—You shouldn't, Herbert.
Mr. White. Herbert always was one for a bit o' fun!

(Herbert *puts bun back on table, comes round in front, and moving the chair out of the way, sits cross-legged on the floor at his father's side.*)

Sergeant. But it's true. Why, if I chose, I could tell you things— But there! you don't get no more yarns out o' me.

Mr. White. Nonsense, old friend. (*Puts down his glass*) You're not going to get shirty about a bit o' fun. (*Moves his chair nearer* Morris's) What was that you started telling me the other day about a monkey's paw, or something? (*Nudges* Herbert, *and winks at* Mrs. White)

Sergeant. (*Gravely*) Nothing. Leastways, nothing worth hearing.

Mrs. White. (*With astonished curiosity*) Monkey's paw—?

Mr. White. Ah—you was tellin' me—

Sergeant. Nothing. Don't go on about it. (*Puts his empty glass to his lips—then stares at it*) What? Empty again? There! When I begin thinkin' o' the paw, it makes me that absent-minded—

Mr. White. (*Rises and fills glass*) You said you always carried it on you.

Sergeant. So I do, for fear o' what might happen. (*Sunk in thought*) Ay!—ay!

Mr. White. (*Handing him his glass refilled*) There. (*Sits again in same chair*)

Mrs. White. What's it for?

Sergeant. You wouldn't believe me, if I was to tell you:

Herbert. I will, every word.

Sergeant. Magic, then!—Don't you laugh!

Herbert. I'm not. Got it on you now?

Sergeant. Of course.

Herbert. Let's see it.

(*Seeing the* Sergeant *embarrassed with his glass,* Mrs. White *rises, takes it from him, places it on mantelpiece, and remains standing.*)

Sergeant. Oh, it's nothing to look at. (*Hunting in his pocket*) Just an ordinary—little paw—dried to a mummy. (*Produces it and holds it towards* Mrs. White) Here.

Mrs. White. (*Who has leant forward eagerly to see it, starts back with a little cry of disgust*) Oh!

Herbert. Give us a look. (Morris *passes the paw to* Mr. White, *from whom* Herbert *takes it.*) Why, it's all dried up!

Sergeant.   I said so.

(*Wind*)

Mrs. White.   (*With a slight shudder*)   Hark at the wind! (*Sits again in her old place*)

Mr. White.   (*Taking the paw from* Herbert)   And what might there be special about it?

Sergeant.   (*Impressively*)   That there paw has had a spell put upon it!

Mr. White.   No? (*In great alarm he thrusts the paw back into* Morris's *hand*.)

Sergeant.   (*Pensively, holding the paw in the palm of his hand*)   Ah! By an old fakir. He was a very holy man. He'd sat all doubled up in one spot, goin' on for fifteen year; thinkin' o' things. And he wanted to show that fate ruled people. That everything was cut and dried from the beginning, as you might say. That there warn't no gettin' away from it. And that, if you tried to, you caught it hot. (*Pauses solemnly*)   So he put a spell on this bit of a paw. It might ha' been anything else, but he took the first thing that came handy. Ah! He put a spell on it, and made it so that three people (*Looking at them and with deep meaning*) could each have three wishes.

(*All but* Mrs. White *laugh rather nervously.*)

Mrs. White.   Ssh! Don't!

Sergeant.   (*More gravely*)   But—! But, mark you, though the wishes was granted, those three people would have cause to wish they *hadn't* been.

Mr. White.   But how *could* the wishes be granted?

Sergeant.   He didn't say. It would all happen so natural, you might think it a coincidence if so disposed.

Herbert.   Why haven't you tried it, sir?

Sergeant.   (*Gravely, after a pause*)   I have.

Herbert.   (*Eagerly*)   You've had your three wishes?

Sergeant.   (*Gravely*)   Yes.

Mrs. White.   Were they granted?

Sergeant.   (*Staring at the fire*)   They were.

(*A pause*)

Mr. White.   Has anybody else wished?

Sergeant.   Yes.   The first owner had his three wish—
(*Lost in recollection*)   Yes, oh yes, he had his three
wishes all right.   I don't know what his first two were,
(*Very impressively*) but the third was for death.   (*All
shudder*)   That's how I got the paw.

(*A pause*)

Herbert.   (*Cheerfully*)   Well!   Seems to me you've only
got to wish for things that *can't* have any bad luck about
'em—   (*Rises*)

Sergeant.   (*Shaking his head*)   Ah!

Mr. White.   (*Tentatively*)   Morris—if you've had your
three wishes—it's no good to you, now—what do you
keep it for?

Sergeant.   (*Still holding the paw; looking at it*)   Fancy,
I s'pose.   I did have some idea of selling it, but I don't
think I will.   It's done mischief enough already.   Besides,
people won't buy.   Some of 'em think it's a fairy tale.
And some want to try it first, and pay after.

(*Nervous laugh from the others*)

Mrs. White.   If you could have another three wishes,
would you?

Sergeant.   (*Slowly—weighing the paw in his hand, and
looking at it*)   I don't know—I don't know—

(*Suddenly, with violence, flinging it in the fire*) No! I'm damned if I would!

(*Movement from all*)

Mr. White. (*Rises and quickly snatches it out of the fire*) What are you doing?

(White *goes right centre.*)

Sergeant. (*Rising and following him and trying to prevent him*) Let it burn! Let the infernal thing burn!

Mrs. White. (*Rises*) Let it burn, father!

Mr. White. (*Wiping it on his coat-sleeve*) No. If you don't want it, give it to me.

Sergeant. (*Violently*) I won't! I won't! My hands are clear of it. I threw it on the fire. If you keep it, don't blame me, whatever happens. Here! Pitch it back again.

Mr. White. (*Stubbornly*) I'm going to keep it. What do you say, Herbert?

Herbert. (*Left centre, laughing*) I say, keep it if you want to. Stuff and nonsense, anyhow.

Mr. White. (*Looking at the paw thoughtfully*) Stuff and nonsense. Yes. I wonder—(*Casually*) I wish—(*He was going to say some ordinary thing, like "I wish I were certain."*)

Sergeant. (*Misunderstanding him; violently*) Stop! Mind what you're doing. That's not the way.

Mr. White. What *is* the way?

Mrs. White. (*Moving away, up right centre to back of table, and beginning to put the tumblers straight, and the chairs in their places*) Oh, don't have anything to do with it, John.

(Takes glasses on tray to dresser, left, busies herself there, rinsing them in a bowl of water on the dresser, and wiping them with a cloth)

Sergeant. That's what I say, marm. But if I warn't to tell him, he might go wishing something he didn't mean to. You hold it in your right hand, and wish aloud. But I warn you! I warn you!

Mrs. White. Sounds like the Arabian Nights. Don't you think you might wish me four pair o' hands?

Mr. White. *(Laughing)* Right you are, mother!—I wish—

Sergeant. *(Pulling his arm down)* Stop it! If you must wish, wish for something sensible. Look here! I can't stand this. Gets on my nerves. Where's my coat? *(Goes into alcove)*

(Mr. White crosses to fireplace and carefully puts the paw on mantelpiece. He is absorbed in it to the end of the tableau.)

Herbert. I'm coming your way, to the works, in a minute. Won't you wait? *(Goes up centre, helps Morris with his coat)*

Sergeant. *(Putting on his coat)* No. I'm all shook up. I want fresh air. I don't want to be here when you wish. And wish you will as soon's my back's turned. I know. I know. But I've warned you, mind.

Mr. White. *(Helping him into his coat)* All right, Morris. Don't you fret about us. *(Gives him money)* Here.

Sergeant. *(Refusing it)* No, I won't—

Mr. White. *(Forcing it into his hand)* Yes, you will. *(Opens door)*

has the paw in his hand.) I don't know what to wish for, and that's a fact. (*He looks about him with a happy smile.*) I seem to've got all I want.

Herbert. (*With his hands on the old man's shoulders*) Old dad! If you'd only cleared the debt on the house, you'd be quite happy, wouldn't you? (*Laughing*) Well—go ahead!—wish for the two hundred pounds: that'll just do it.

Mr. White. (*Half laughing*) Shall I?

(*Crosses to right centre*)

Herbert. Go on! Here!—I'll play slow music. (*Crosses to piano*)

Mrs. White. Don't 'ee, John. Don't have nothing to do with it!

Herbert. Now, dad! (*Plays*)

Mr. White. I will! (*Holds up the paw, as if half ashamed*) I wish for two hundred pounds.

(*Crash on the piano; at the same instant* Mr. White *utters a cry and lets the paw drop.*)

Mrs. White
    and   }   What's the matter?
Herbert.

Mr. White. (*Gazing with horror at the paw*) It moved! As I wished, it twisted in my hand like a snake.

Herbert. (*Goes down right, and picks the paw up*) Nonsense, dad. Why, it's as stiff as a bone. (*Lays it on the mantelpiece*)

Mrs. White. Must have been your fancy, father.

Herbert. (*Laughing*) Well—? (*Looking round the room*) I don't see the money; and I bet I never shall.

Mr. White. (*Relieved*) Thank God, there's no harm done! But it gave me a shock.

Sergeant. (*Turning to the room*) Well, good-
(*To* White) Put it in the fire.

All. Good-night.

(*Exit* Sergeant; Mr. White *closes door, comes towa*
fireplace, absorbed in the paw.)

Herbert. (*Down left*) If there's no more in this
there is in his other stories, we shan't make much
of it.

Mrs. White. (*Comes down right centre to* White) D
you give him anything for it, father?

Mr. White. A trifle. He didn't want it, but I mad
him take it.

Mrs. White. There, now! You shouldn't. Throwing
your money about.

Mr. White. (*Looking at the paw which he has picked
up again*) I wonder—

Herbert. What?

Mr. White. I wonder, whether we hadn't better chuck
it on the fire?

Herbert. (*Laughing*) Likely! Why, we're all going
to be rich and famous, and happy.

Mrs. White. Throw it on the fire, indeed, when you've
given money for it! So like you, father.

Herbert. Wish to be an Emperor, father, to begin with.
Then you can't be henpecked!

Mrs. White. (*Going for him, front of table, with a duster*)
You young—! (*Follows him to back of table*)

Herbert. (*Running away from her round behind table*)
Steady with that duster, mother!

Mr. White. Be quiet, there! (Herbert *catches* Mrs.
White *in his arms and kisses her.*) I wonder— (*He*

Herbert. Half-past eleven. I must get along. I'm on at midnight. (*Goes up centre, fetches his coat, etc.*) We've had quite a merry evening.

Mrs. White. I'm off to bed. Don't be late for breakfast, Herbert.

Herbert. I shall walk home as usual. Does me good. I shall be with you about nine. Don't wait, though.

Mrs. White. You know your father never waits.

Herbert. Good-night, mother. (*Kisses her; she lights candle on dresser, left, goes up stairs; exit*)

Herbert. (*Coming to his father, right, who is sunk in thought*) Good-night, dad. You'll find the cash tied up in the middle of the bed.

Mr. White. (*Staring, seizes* Herbert's *hand*) It moved, Herbert.

Herbert. Ah! And a monkey hanging by his tail from the bed-post, watching you count the golden sovereigns.

Mr. White. (*Accompanying him to the door*) I wish you wouldn't joke, my boy.

Herbert. All right, dad. (*Opens door*) Lord! What weather! Good-night. (*Exit*)

(*The old man shakes his head, closes the door, locks it, puts the chain up, slips the lower bolt, has some difficulty with the upper bolt.*)

Mr. White. This bolt's stiff again! I must get Herbert to look to it in the morning.

(*Comes into the room, puts out the lamp, crosses towards steps but is irresistibly attracted towards fireplace; sits down and stares into the fire; his expression changes; he sees something horrible.*)

Mr. White. (*With an involuntary cry*) Mother! Mother!

Mrs. White. (*Appearing at the door at the top of the steps with candle*) What's the matter? (*Comes down right centre*)

Mr. White. (*Mastering himself, rises*) Nothing — I — haha!—I saw faces in the fire.

Mrs. White. Come along.

(*She takes his arm and draws him towards the steps. He looks back frightened towards fireplace as they reach the first step.*)

Tableau Curtain

II

(*Bright sunshine; the table, which has been moved nearer the window, is laid for breakfast. Mrs. White busy about the table; Mr. White standing in the window looking off right; the inner door is open, showing the outer door.*)

Mr. White. What a morning Herbert's got for walking home!

Mrs. White. (*Left centre*) What's o'clock? (*Looks at clock on mantelpiece*) Quarter to nine, I declare. He's off at eight. (*Crosses to fire*)

Mr. White. Takes him half-an-hour to change and wash. He's just by the cemetery now.

Mrs. White. He'll be here in ten minutes.

Mr. White. (*Coming to the table*) What's for breakfast?

Mrs. White. Sausages. (*At the mantelpiece*) Why, if here isn't that dirty monkey's paw! (*Picks it up, looks at it with disgust, puts it back; takes sausages in dish from before fire and places them on table*) Silly thing! The idea of us listening to such nonsense!

Mr. White. (*Goes up to window again*) Ay—the

Sergeant-Major and his yarns! I suppose all old soldiers are alike—

Mrs. White. Come on, father. Herbert hates us to wait.

(They both sit and begin breakfast.)

Mrs. White. How could wishes be granted, nowadays?

Mr. White. Ah! Been thinking about it all night, have you?

Mrs. White. You kept me awake, with your tossing and tumbling—

Mr. White. Ay, I had a bad night.

Mrs. White. It was the storm, I expect. How it blew!

Mr. White. I didn't hear it. I was asleep and not asleep, if you know what I mean.

Mrs. White. And all that rubbish about its making you unhappy if your wish *was* granted! How could two hundred pounds hurt you, eh, father?

Mr. White. Might drop on my head in a lump. Don't see any other way. And I'd try to bear that. Though, mind you, Morris said it would all happen so naturally that you might take it for a coincidence, if so disposed.

Mrs. White. Well—it hasn't happened. That's all I know. And it isn't going to. *(A letter is seen to drop in the letter-box.)* And how you can sit there and talk about it— *(Sharp postman's knock; she jumps to her feet.)* What's that?

Mr. White. Postman, o' course.

Mrs. White. *(Seeing the letter from a distance; in an awed whisper)* He's brought a letter, John!

Mr. White. *(Laughing)* What did you think he'd bring? Ton o' coals?

Mrs. White. John—! John—! Suppose—?

Mr. White.   Suppose what?

Mrs. White.   Suppose it was two hundred pounds!

Mr. White.   (*Suppressing his excitement*)   Eh!—Here! Don't talk nonsense.   Why don't you fetch it?

Mrs. White.   (*Crosses and takes letter out of the box*)   It's thick, John— (*Feels it*)—and—and it's got something crisp inside it.   (*Takes letter to* White, *right centre*)

Mr. White.   Who—who's it for?

Mrs. White.   You.

Mr. White.   Hand it over, then.   (*Feeling and examining it with ill-concealed excitement*)   The idea!   What a superstitious old woman you are!   Where are my specs?

Mrs. White.   Let me open it.

Mr. White.   Don't you touch it.   Where are my specs?

                              (*Goes to right*)

Mrs. White.   Don't let sudden wealth sour your temper, John.

Mr. White.   *Will* you find my specs?

Mrs. White.   (*Taking them off mantelpiece*)   Here, John, here.   (*As he opens the letter*)   Take care!   Don't tear it!

Mr. White.   Tear what?

Mrs. White.   If it was banknotes, John!

✱**Mr. White.**   (*Taking a thick, formal document out of the envelope and a crisp-looking slip*)   You've gone dotty. —You've made me nervous.   (*Reads*)   "Sir,—Enclosed please find receipt for interest on the mortgage of £200 on your house, duly received."

(*They look at each other.*   Mr. White *sits down to finish his breakfast silently.*   Mrs. White *goes to the window.*)

Mrs. White. That comes of listening to tipsy old soldiers.

Mr. White. (*Pettish*) What does?

Mrs. White. You thought there was banknotes in it.

Mr. White. (*Injured*) I didn't! I said all along—

Mrs. White. How Herbert will laugh, when I tell him!

Mr. White. (*With gruff good-humour*) You're not going to tell him. You're going to keep your mouth shut. That's what you're going to do. Why, I should never hear the last of it.

Mrs. White. Serve you right. I shall tell him. You know you like his fun. See how he joked you last night when you said the paw moved.

(*She is looking through the window towards right centre.*)

Mr. White. So it did. It did move. That I'll swear to.

Mrs. White. (*Abstractedly: she is watching something outside.*) You thought it did.

Mr. White. I say it did. There was no thinking about it. You saw how it upset me, didn't you?

(*She doesn't answer.*)

Didn't you?—Why don't you listen? (*Turns round*) What is it?

Mrs. White. Nothing.

Mr. White. (*Turns back to his breakfast*) Do you see Herbert coming?

Mrs. White. No.

Mr. White. He's about due. What *is* it?

Mrs. White. Nothing. Only a man. Looks like a gentleman. Leastways, he's in black, and he's got a top-hat on.

Mr. White.   What about him?   (*He is not interested; goes on eating*)

Mrs. White.   He stood at the garden-gate as if he wanted to come in.   But he couldn't seem to make up his mind.

Mr. White.   Oh, go on!   You're full o' fancies.

Mrs. White.   He's going—no; he's coming back.

Mr. White.   Don't let him see you peeping.

Mrs. White.   (*With increasing excitement*) He's looking at the house.   He's got his hand on the latch.   No. He turns away again.   (*Eagerly*) John! He looks like a sort of a lawyer.

Mr. White.   What of it?

Mrs. White.   Oh, you'll only laugh again.   But suppose —suppose he's coming about the two hundred—

Mr. White.   You're not to mention it again!—You're a foolish old woman.—Come and eat your breakfast. (*Eagerly*)   Where is he now?

Mrs. White.   Gone down the road.   He has turned back. He seems to've made up his mind.   Here he comes!— Oh, John, and me all untidy!   (*Crosses to fire, right*)

(*Knock*)

Mr. White.   (*To Mrs. White, who is hastily smoothing her hair, etc.*)   What's it matter?   He's made a mistake. Come to the wrong house.   (*Crosses to fireplace*)

(Mrs. White *opens the door.* Mr. Sampson, *dressed from head to foot in solemn black, with a top-hat, stands in the doorway.*)

Sampson.   (*Outside*)   Is this Mr. White's?

Mrs. White.   Come in, sir.   Please step in.

(*She shows him into the room, goes right; he is awkward and nervous.*)

You must overlook our being so untidy; and the room all anyhow; and John in his garden-coat. (*To* Mr. White, *reproachfully*) Oh, John.

Sampson. (*To* Mr. White) Morning. My name is Sampson.

Mrs. White. (*Offering a chair*) Won't you please be seated?

(Sampson *stands quite still up centre.*)

Sampson. Ah—thank you—no, I think not—I think not. (*Pause*)

Mr. White. (*Awkwardly, trying to help him*) Fine weather for the time o' year.

Sampson. Ah—yes—yes— (*Pause; he makes a renewed effort.*) My name is Sampson—I've come—

Mrs. White. Perhaps you was wishful to see Herbert; he'll be home in a minute. (*Pointing*) Here's his breakfast waiting—

Sampson. (*Interrupting her hastily*) No, no! (*Pause*) I've come from the electrical works—

Mrs. White. Why, you might have come *with* him.

(Mr. White *sees something is wrong, tenderly puts his hand on her arm.*)

Sampson. No—no—I've come—*alone*.

Mrs. White. (*With a little anxiety*) Is anything the matter?

Sampson. I was asked to call—

Mrs. White. (*Abruptly*) Herbert! Has anything happened? Is he hurt? Is he hurt?

Mr. White. (*Soothing her*) There, there, mother. Don't you jump to conclusions. Let the gentleman speak. You've not brought bad news, I'm sure, sir.

Sampson. I'm—sorry—

Mrs. White. Is he hurt?

(Sampson *bows.*)

Mrs. White. Badly?

Sampson. Very badly. (*Turns away*).

Mrs. White. (*With a cry*) John—! (*She instinctively moves towards* White.)

Mr. White. Is he in pain?

Sampson. He is not in pain.

Mrs. White. Oh, thank God! Thank God for that! Thank— (*She looks in a startled fashion at* Mr. White— *realizes what* Sampson *means, catches his arm and tries to turn him towards her.*) Do you mean—?

(Sampson *avoids her look. She gropes for her husband: he takes her two hands in his, and gently lets her sink into the armchair above the fireplace, then he stands on her right, between her and* Sampson.)

Mr. White. (*Hoarsely*) Go on, sir.

Sampson. He was telling his mates a story. Something that had happened here last night. He was laughing, and wasn't noticing and—and— (*Hushed*) the machinery caught him—

(*A little cry from* Mrs. White; *her face shows her horror and agony.*)

Mr. White. (*Vague, holding* Mrs. White's *hand*) The machinery caught him—yes—and him the only child— it's hard, sir—very hard—

Sampson. (*Subdued*). The Company wished me to convey their sincere sympathy with you in your great loss—

Mr. White. (*Staring blankly*) Our—great—loss—!

Sampson. I was to say further—(*As if apologizing*) I am
only their servant—I am only obeying orders—

Mr. White. Our—great—loss—

Sampson. (*Laying an envelope on the table and edging
towards the door*) I was to say, the Company disclaim
all responsibility, but, in consideration of your son's
services, they wish to present you with a certain sum as
compensation. (*Gets to door*)

Mr. White. Our—great—loss— (*Suddenly, with horror*)
How—how much?

Sampson. (*In the doorway*) Two hundred pounds.

(*Exit*)

(Mrs. White *gives a cry. The old man takes no heed
of her, smiles faintly, puts out his hands like a sightless
man, and drops, a senseless heap, to the floor.* Mrs. White
*stares at him blankly and her hands go out helplessly
towards him.*)

Tableau Curtain

III

(*Night; on the table a candle is flickering at its last
gasp. The room looks neglected.* Mr. White *is dozing
fitfully in the armchair.* Mrs. White *is in the window
peering through the blind towards left.*)

(Mr. White *starts, wakes, looks around him.*)

Mr. White. (*Fretfully*) Jenny—Jenny.

Mrs. White. (*In the window*) Yes.

Mr. White. Where are you?

Mrs. White. At the window.

Mr. White. What are you doing?

Mrs. White. Looking up the road.

Mr. White. (*Falling back*) What's the use, Jenny? What's the use?

Mrs. White. That's where the cemetery is; that's where we've laid him.

Mr. White. Ay—ay—a week to-day—what o'clock is it?

Mrs. White. I don't know.

Mr. White. We don't take much account of time now, Jenny, do we?

Mrs. White. Why should we? He don't come home. He'll never come home again. There's nothing to think about—

Mr. White. Or to talk about. (*Pause*) Come away from the window; you'll get cold.

Mrs. White. It's colder where *he* is.

Mr. White. Ay—gone for ever—

Mrs. White. And taken all our hopes with him—

Mr. White. And all our *wishes*—

Mrs. White. Ay, and all our— (*With a sudden cry*) John!

(*She comes quickly to him; he rises.*)

Mr. White. Jenny! For God's sake! What's the matter?

Mrs. White. (*With dreadful eagerness*) The *paw*! The monkey's paw!

Mr. White. (*Bewildered*) Where? Where is it? What's wrong with it?

Mrs. White. I want it! You haven't done away with it?

Mr. White. I haven't seen it—since—why?

Mrs. White. I want it! Find it! Find it!

Mr. White. (*Groping on the mantelpiece*) Here! Here it is! What do you want of it? (*He leaves it there.*)

Mrs. White. Why didn't I think of it? Why didn't *you* think of it?

Mr. White. Think of what?

Mrs. White. The *other two* wishes!

Mr. White. (*With horror*) What?

Mrs. White. We've only had one.

Mr. White. (*Tragically*) Wasn't that enough?

Mrs. White. No! We'll have one more. (White *crosses to right centre*. Mrs. White *takes the paw and follows him.*) Take it. Take it quickly. And wish—

Mr. White. (*Avoiding the paw*) Wish what?

Mrs. White. Oh, John! John! Wish our boy alive again!

Mr. White. Good God! Are you mad?

Mrs. White. Take it. Take it and wish. (*With a paroxysm of grief*) Oh, my boy! My boy!

Mr. White. Get to bed. Get to sleep. You don't know what you're saying.

Mrs. White. We had the first wish granted—why not the second?

Mr. White. (*Hushed*) He's been dead ten days, and— Jenny! Jenny! I only knew him by his clothing—if you wasn't allowed to see him then—how could you bear to see him *now*?

Mrs. White. I don't care. Bring him back.

Mr. White. (*Shrinking from the paw*) I daren't touch it!

Mrs. White. (*Thrusting it in his hand*) Here! Here! Wish!

Mr. White. (*Trembling*) Jenny!

Mrs. White. (*Fiercely*) Wish. (*She goes on frantically whispering "Wish."*)

Mr. White. (*Shuddering, but overcome by her insistence*) I—I—wish—my—son—alive again.

(*He drops it with a cry. The candle goes out. Utter darkness; he sinks into a chair. Mrs. White hurries to the window and draws the blind back. She stands in the moonlight. Pause*)

Mrs. White. (*Drearily*) Nothing.

Mr. White. Thank God! Thank God!

Mrs. White. Nothing at all. Along the whole length of the road not a living thing. (*Closes blind*) And nothing, nothing, nothing left in our lives, John.

Mr. White. Except each other, Jenny—and memories.

Mrs. White. (*Coming back slowly to the fireplace*) We're too old. We were only alive in him. We can't begin again. We can't feel anything now, John, but emptiness and darkness. (*She sinks into armchair.*)

Mr. White. 'Tisn't for long, Jenny. There's that to look forward to.

Mrs. White. Every minute's long, now.

Mr. White. (*Rising*) I can't bear the darkness!

Mrs. White. It's dreary—dreary.

Mr. White. (*Crosses to dresser*) Where's the candle? (*Finds it and brings it to table*) And the matches? Where are the matches? We mustn't sit in the dark. 'Tisn't wholesome. (*Lights match; the other candlestick is close to him.*) There. (*Turning with the lighted match towards* Mrs. White, *who is rocking and moaning*) Don't take on so, mother.

Mrs. White. I'm a mother no longer.

Mr. White. (*Lights candle*) There now; there now. Go on up to bed. Go on, now—I'm a-coming.

Mrs. White. Whether I'm here or in bed, or wherever I am, I'm with my boy, I'm with—

(*A low single knock at the street door*)

Mrs. White. (*Starting*) What's that!

Mr. White. (*Mastering his horror*) A rat. The house is full of 'em. (*A louder single knock; she starts up. He catches her by the arm.*) Stop! What are you going to do?

Mrs. White. (*Wildly*) It's my boy! It's Herbert! I forgot it was a mile away! What are you holding me for? I must open the door!

(*The knocking continues in single knocks at irregular intervals, constantly growing louder and more insistent.*)

Mr. White. (*Still holding her*) For God's sake!

Mrs. White. (*Struggling*) Let me go!

Mr. White. Don't open the door!

(*He drags her towards left front.*)

Mrs. White. Let me go!

Mr. White. Think what you might see!

Mrs. White. (*Struggling fiercely*) Do you think I fear the child I bore! Let me go! (*She wrenches herself loose and rushes to the door, which she tears open.*) I'm coming, Herbert! I'm coming!

Mr. White. (*Cowering in the extreme corner, left front*) Don't 'ee do it! Don't 'ee do it!

(Mrs. White *is at work on the outer door, where the knocking still continues. She slips the chain, slips the lower bolt, unlocks the door.*)

Mr. White. (*Suddenly*) The paw! Where's the monkey's paw?

(*He gets on his knees and feels along the floor for it.*)

Mrs. White. (*Tugging at the top bolt*) John! The top bolt's stuck. I can't move it. Come and help. Quick!

Mr. White. (*Wildly groping*) The paw! There's a wish left.

(*The knocking is now loud, and in groups of increasing length between the speeches.*)

Mrs. White. D'ye hear him? John! Your child's knocking!

Mr. White. Where is it? Where did it fall?

Mrs. White. (*Tugging desperately at the bolt*) Help! Help! Will you keep your child from his home?

Mr. White. Where did it fall? I can't find it—I can't find—

(*The knocking is now tempestuous and there are blows upon the door as of a body beating against it.*)

Mrs. White. Herbert! Herbert! My boy! Wait! Your mother's opening to you! Ah! It's moving! It's moving!

Mr. White. God forbid! (*Finds the paw*) Ah!

Mrs. White. (*Slipping the bolt*) Herbert!

Mr. White. (*Has raised himself to his knees; he holds the paw high.*) I wish him dead. (*The knocking stops abruptly.*) I wish him dead and at peace!

Mrs. White. (*Flinging the door open simultaneously*) Herb—

(*A flood of moonlight; emptiness; the old man sways in prayer on his knees. The old woman lies half swooning, wailing against the door-post.*)

CURTAIN

The Happy Journey

by THORNTON WILDER

CHARACTERS

The Stage Manager

Ma Kirby

Arthur (*thirteen*)

Caroline (*fifteen*)

Pa (Elmer) Kirby

Beulah (*twenty-two*)

THE SCENE

No scenery is required for this play. The idea is that no place is being represented. This may be achieved by a grey curtain backdrop with no sidepieces; a cyclorama; or the empty bare stage.

All properties, except two, are imaginary. One of these is the automobile, which is made up of four chairs on a low platform. The second is an ordinary cot.

THE HAPPY JOURNEY

(*As the curtain rises,* The Stage Manager *is leaning lazily against the proscenium pillar at the left. He is smoking. Arthur is playing marbles down center in pantomime. Caroline is way up left talking to some girls who are invisible to us. Ma Kirby is anxiously putting on her hat (real) before an imaginary mirror up right.*)

Ma. Where's your pa? Why isn't he here? I declare we'll never get started.

Arthur. Ma, where's my hat? I guess I don't go if I can't find my hat. (*Still playing marbles*)

Ma. Go out into the hall and see if it isn't there. Where's Caroline gone to now, the plagued child?

Arthur. She's out waitin' in the street talkin' to the Jones girls.—I just looked in the hall a thousand times, Ma, and it isn't there. (*He spits for good luck before a difficult shot and mutters:*) Come on, baby.

Ma. Go and look again, I say. Look carefully.

(Arthur *rises, reluctantly crosses right, turns around, returns swiftly to his game center, flinging himself on the floor with a terrible impact and starts shooting an aggie.*)

Arthur. No, Ma, it's not there.

Ma. (*Serenely*) Well, you don't leave Newark without that hat, make up your mind to that. I don't go no journeys with a hoodlum.

Arthur. Aw, Ma!

(Ma *comes down right, to the footlights, pulls up an imaginary window, and talks towards the audience.*)

Ma. (*Calling*) Oh, Mrs. Schwartz!

The Stage Manager. (*Down left; consulting his script*) Here I am, Mrs. Kirby. Are you going yet?

Ma. I guess we're going in just a minute. How's the baby?

The Stage Manager. She's all right now. We slapped her on the back and she spat it up.

Ma. Isn't that fine!—Well, now, if you'll be good enough to give the cat a saucer of milk in the morning and the evening, Mrs. Schwartz, I'll be ever so grateful to you.—Oh, good-afternoon, Mrs. Hobmeyer!

The Stage Manager. Good-afternoon, Mrs. Kirby, I hear you're going away.

Ma. (*Modest*) Oh, just for three days, Mrs. Hobmeyer, to see my married daughter, Beulah, in Camden. Elmer's got his vacation week from the laundry early this year, and he's just the best driver in the world.

(Caroline *comes down stage right and stands by her mother.*)

The Stage Manager. Is the whole family going?

Ma. Yes, all four of us that's here. The change ought to be good for the children. My married daughter was downright sick a while ago—

The Stage Manager. Tchk—tchk—tchk! Yes. I remember you tellin' us.

Ma. (*With feeling*) And I just want to go down and see the child. I ain't seen her since then. I just won't rest easy in my mind without I see her. (*To* Caroline) Can't you say good-afternoon to Mrs. Hobmeyer?

Caroline. (*Lowers her eyes and says woodenly*) Good-afternoon, Mrs. Hobmeyer.

The Stage Manager. Good-afternoon, dear.—Well, I'll wait and beat these rugs until after you're gone, because I don't want to choke you. I hope you have a good time and find everything all right.

Ma. Thank you, Mrs. Hobmeyer, I hope I will.— Well, I guess that milk for the cat is all, Mrs. Schwartz, if you're sure you don't mind. If anything should come up, the key to the back door is hanging by the icebox.

Caroline. Ma! Not so loud.

Arthur. Everybody can hear yuh.

Ma. Stop pullin' my dress, children. (*In a loud whisper*) The key to the back door I'll leave hangin' by the icebox and I'll leave the screen door unhooked.

The Stage Manager. Now have a good trip, dear, and give my love to Beuhly.

Ma. I will, and thank you a thousand times. (*She lowers the window, turns up stage, and looks around. Caroline goes left and vigorously rubs her cheeks. Ma occupies herself with the last touches of packing.*) What can be keeping your pa?

Arthur. (*Who has not left his marbles*) I can't find my hat, Ma.

       (*Enter* Elmer *holding a cap, up right*)

Elmer. Here's Arthur's hat. He musta left it in the car Sunday.

Ma. That's a mercy. Now we can start.—Caroline Kirby, what you done to your cheeks?

Caroline. (*Defiant-abashed*) Nothin'.

Ma. If you've put anything on 'em, I'll slap you:

Caroline. No, Ma, of course I haven't. (*Hanging her head*) I just rubbed 'm to make 'm red. All the girls do that at High School when they're goin' places.

Ma. Such silliness I never saw. Elmer, what kep' you?

Elmer. (*Always even-voiced and always looking out a little anxiously through his spectacles*) I just went to the garage and had Charlie give a last look at it, Kate.

Ma. I'm glad you did. (*Collecting two pieces of imaginary luggage and starting for the door*) I wouldn't like to have no breakdown miles from anywhere. Now we can start. Arthur, put those marbles away. Anybody'd think you didn't want to go on a journey to look at yuh.

(*They go out through the "hall." Ma opens an imaginary door down right. Pa, Caroline, and Arthur go through it. Ma follows, taking time to lock the door, hang the key by the "icebox." They turn up at an abrupt angle, going up stage. As they come to the steps from the back porch, each, arriving at a given point, starts bending his knees lower and lower to denote going downstairs, and find themselves in the street. The Stage Manager moves the automobile from the right. It is right center of the stage, seen partially at an angle, its front pointing down center.*)

Elmer. (*Coming forward*) Here, you boys, you keep away from that car.

Ma. Those Sullivan boys put their heads into everything.

(*They get into the car. Elmer's hands hold an imaginary steering wheel and continually shift gears. Ma sits beside him. Arthur is behind him and Caroline is behind Ma.*

Caroline. (*Standing up in the back seat, waving, self-consciously*) Good-bye, Mildred. Good-bye, Helen.

The Stage Manager. (*Having returned to his position by the left proscenium*) Good-bye, Caroline. Good-bye, Mrs. Kirby. I hope y' have a good time.

Ma. Good-bye, girls.

The Stage Manager. Good-bye, Kate. The car looks fine.

Ma. (*Looking upward towards a window right*) Oh, good-bye, Emma! (*Modestly*) We think it's the best little Chevrolet in the world.— (*Looking up towards the left*) Oh, good-bye, Mrs. Adler!

The Stage Manager. What, are you going away, Mrs. Kirby?

Ma. Just for three days, Mrs. Adler, to see my married daughter in Camden.

The Stage Manager. Have a good time.

(*Now* Ma, Caroline, *and* The Stage Manager *break out into a tremendous chorus of good-byes. The whole street is saying good-bye.* Arthur *takes out his peashooter and lets fly happily into the air. There is a lurch or two and they are off.*)

Arthur. (*Leaning forward in sudden fright*) Pa! Pa! Don't go by the school. Mr. Biedenbach might see us!

Ma. I don't care if he does see us. I guess I can take my children out of school for one day without having to hide down back streets about it. (Elmer *nods to a passerby. Without sharpness*) Who was that you spoke to, Elmer?

Elmer. That was the fellow who arranges our banquets down to the Lodge, Kate.

Ma. Is he the one who had to buy four hundred steaks? (Pa *nods.*) I declare, I'm glad I'm not him.

Elmer. The air's getting better already. Take deep breaths, children.

(*They inhale noisily.*)

Arthur. (*Pointing to a sign and indicating that it gradually goes by*) Gee, it's almost open fields already. "*Weber and Heilbronner Suits for Well-dressed Men.*" Ma, can I have one of them some day?

Ma. If you graduate with good marks perhaps your father'll let you have one for graduation.

(*Pause; general gazing about, then sudden lurch*)

Caroline. (*Whining*) Oh, Pa! do we have to wait while that whole funeral goes by?

(Elmer *takes off his hat.* Ma *cranes forward with absorbed curiosity.*)

Ma. (*Not sharp and bossy*) Take off your hat, Arthur. Look at your father.—Why, Elmer, I do believe that's a lodge-brother of yours. See the banner? I suppose this is the Elizabeth branch. (Elmer *nods.* Ma *sighs: Tchk—tchk—tchk. The children lean forward and all watch the funeral in silence, growing momentarily more solemnized. After a pause,* Ma *continues almost dreamily but not sentimentally.*) Well, we haven't forgotten the funeral that we went on, have we? We haven't forgotten our good Harold. He gave his life for his country, we mustn't forget that. (*There is another pause; with cheerful resignation*) Well, we'll all hold up the traffic for a few minutes some day.

The Children. (*Very uncomfortable*) Ma!

Ma. (*Without self-pity*) Well, I'm "ready," children. I hope everybody in this car is "ready." And I pray to go first, Elmer. Yes.

(Elmer *touches her hand.*)

Caroline. Ma, everybody's looking at you.

Arthur. Everybody's laughing at you.

Ma. Oh, hold your tongues! I don't care what a lot of silly people in Elizabeth, New Jersey, think of me. —Now we can go on. That's the last.

(There is another lurch and the car goes on.)

Caroline. *(Looking at a sign and turning as she passes it)* "Fit-Rite Suspenders. The Working Man's Choice." Pa, why do they spell Rite that way?

Elmer. So that it'll make you stop and ask about it, Missy.

Caroline. Papa, you're teasing me.—Ma, why do they say "*Three Hundred Rooms Three Hundred Baths*"?

Arthur. "*Miller's Spaghetti: The Family's Favorite Dish.*" Ma, why don't you ever have spaghetti?

Ma. Go along, you'd never eat it.

Arthur. Ma, I like it now.

Caroline. *(With gesture)* Yum-yum. It looked wonderful up there. Ma, make some when we get home?

Ma. *(Dryly)* "The management is always happy to receive suggestions. We aim to please."

(The children scream with laughter. Even Elmer smiles. Ma remains modest.)

Elmer. Well, I guess no one's complaining, Kate. Everybody knows you're a good cook.

Ma. I don't know whether I'm a good cook or not, but I know I've had practice. At least I've cooked three meals a day for twenty-five years.

Arthur. Aw, Ma, you went out to eat once in a while.

Ma. Yes. That made it a leap year.

(The children laugh again.)

Caroline. (*In an ecstasy of well-being puts her arms around her mother*) Ma, I love going out in the country like this. Let's do it often, Ma.

Ma. Goodness, smell that air, will you! It's got the whole ocean in it.—Elmer, drive careful over that bridge. This must be New Brunswick we're coming to.

Arthur. (*After a slight pause*) Ma, when is the next comfort station?

Ma. (*Unruffled*) You don't want one. You just said that to be awful.

Caroline. (*Shrilly*) Yes, he did, Ma. He's terrible. He says that kind of thing right out in school and I want to sink through the floor, Ma. He's terrible.

Ma. Oh, don't get so excited about nothing, Miss Proper! I guess we're all yewman beings in this car, at least as far as I know. And, Arthur, you try and be a gentleman.—Elmer, don't run over that collie dog. (*She follows the dog with her eyes.*) Looked kinda peakèd to me. Needs a good honest bowl of leavings. Pretty dog, too. (*Her eyes fall on a billboard at the right.*) That's a pretty advertisement for Chesterfield cigarettes, isn't it? Looks like Beulah, a little.

Arthur. Ma?

Ma. Yes.

Arthur. (*"Route" rhymes with "out."*) Can't I take a paper route with the Newark *Daily Post*?

Ma. No, you cannot. No, sir. I hear they make the paper boys get up at four-thirty in the morning. No son of mine is going to get up at four-thirty every morning, not if it's to make a million dollars. Your *Saturday Evening Post* route on Thursday mornings is enough.

Arthur. Aw, Ma.

Ma. No, sir. No son of mine is going to get up at four-thirty and miss the sleep God meant him to have.

Arthur. (*Sullenly*) Hhm! Ma's always talking about God. I guess she got a letter from Him this morning.

Ma. (*Outraged*) Elmer, stop that automobile this minute. I don't go another step with anybody that says things like that. Athur, you get out of this car. (Elmer *stops the car.*) Elmer, you give him a dollar bill. He can go back to Newark by himself. I don't want him.

Arthur. What did I say? There wasn't anything terrible about that.

Elmer. I didn't hear what he said, Kate.

Ma. God has done a lot of things for me and I won't have Him made fun of by anybody. Get out of this car this minute.

Caroline. Aw, Ma,—don't spoil the ride.

Ma. No.

Elmer. We might as well go on, Kate, since we've got started. I'll talk to the boy tonight.

Ma. (*Slowly conceding*) All right, if you say so, Elmer.

(Elmer *starts the car.*)

Arthur. (*Frightened*) Aw, Ma, that wasn't so terrible.

Ma. I don't want to talk about it. I hope your father washes your mouth out with soap and water.—Where'd we all be if I started talking about God like that, I'd like to know! We'd be in the speak-easies and night-clubs and places like that, that's where we'd be.

Caroline. (*After a very slight pause*) What did he say, Ma? I didn't hear what he said.

Ma. I don't want to talk about it.

(*They drive on in silence for a moment, the shocked silence after a scandal.*)

Elmer. I'm going to stop and give the car a little water, I guess.

Ma. All right, Elmer. You know best.

Elmer. (*Turns the wheel and stops; as to a garage hand*) Could I have a little water in the radiator—to make sure?

The Stage Manager. (*In this scene alone he lays aside his script and enters into a rôle seriously.*) You sure can. (*He punches the left front tire.*) Air all right? Do you need any oil or gas? (*Goes up around car*)

Elmer. No, I think not. I just got fixed up in Newark. (The Stage Manager *carefully pours some water into the hood.*)

Ma. We're on the right road for Camden, are we?

The Stage Manager. (*Coming down on right side of car*) Yes, keep straight ahead. You can't miss it. You'll be in Trenton in a few minutes. Camden's a great town, lady, believe me.

Ma. My daughter likes it fine,—my married daughter.

The Stage Manager. Ye'? It's a great burg all right. I guess I think so because I was born near there.

Ma. Well, well. Your folks still live there?

The Stage Manager. (*Standing with one foot on the rung of* Ma's *chair; they have taken a great fancy to one another.*) No, my old man sold the farm and they built a factory on it. So the folks moved to Philadelphia.

Ma. My married daughter Beulah lives there because her husband works in the telephone company.—Stop pokin' me, Caroline!—We're all going down to see her for a few days.

The Stage Manager. Ye'?

Ma. She's been sick, you see, and I just felt I had to go and see her. My husband and my boy are going to stay at the **Y.M.C.A:** I hear they've got a dormitory on the top floor that's real clean and comfortable. Had you ever been there?

The Stage Manager. No. I'm Knights of Columbus myself.

Ma. Oh.

The Stage Manager. I used to play basketball at the Y though. It looked all right to me. (*He reluctantly moves away and pretends to examine the car again.*) Well, I guess you're all set now, lady. I hope you have a good trip; you can't miss it.

Everybody. Thanks. Thanks a lot. Good luck to you.

(Jolts and lurches)

Ma. (*With a sigh*) The world's full of nice people.— That's what I call a nice young man.

Caroline. (*Earnestly*) Ma, you oughtn't to tell 'm all everything about yourself.

Ma. Well, Caroline, you do your way and I'll do mine. —He looked kinda pale to me. I'd like to feed him up for a few days. His mother lives in Philadelphia and I expects he eats at those dreadful Greek places.

Caroline. I'm hungry. Pa, there's a hot dog stand. K'n I have one?

Elmer. We'll all have one, eh, Kate? We had such an early lunch.

Ma. Just as you think best, Elmer.

(Elmer *stops the car.*)

Elmer. Arthur, here's half a dollar.—Run over and see what they have. Not too much mustard either.

(Arthur *descends from the car and goes off stage right.* Ma *and* Caroline *get out and walk a bit, up stage and to the left.* Caroline *keeps at her mother's right.*)

Ma. What's that flower over there?—I'll take some of those to Beulah.

Caroline. It's just a weed, Ma.

Ma. I like it.—My, look at the sky, wouldya! I'm glad I was born in New Jersey. I've always said it was the best state in the Union. Every state has something no other state has got.

(*Presently* Arthur *returns with his hands full of imaginary hot dogs, which he distributes. First to his father, next to* Caroline, *who comes forward to meet him, and lastly to his mother; he is still very much cast down by the recent scandal, and as he approaches his mother, says falteringly:*)

Arthur. Ma, I'm sorry. I'm sorry for what I said. (*He bursts into tears.*)

Ma. There. There. We all say wicked things at times. I know you didn't mean it like it sounded. (*He weeps still more violently than before.*) Why, now, now! I forgive you, Arthur, and tonight before you go to bed you . . . (*She whispers.*) You're a good boy at heart, Arthur, and we all know it. (Caroline *starts to cry too.* Ma *is suddenly joyously alive and happy.*) Sakes alive, it's too nice a day for us all to be cryin'. Come now, get in. (*Crossing behind car to the right side, followed by the children*) Caroline, go up in front with your father. Ma wants to sit with her beau. (Caroline *sits in front with her father.* Ma *lets* Arthur *get in car ahead of her; then she closes door.*) I never saw such children. Your hot dogs are all getting wet. Now chew them fine, everybody—All right, Elmer, forward march. (*Car starts.* Caroline *spits.*) Caroline, whatever are you doing?

Caroline. I'm spitting out the leather, Ma.

Ma. Then say: Excuse me.

Caroline. Excuse me, please. (*She spits again.*)

Ma. What's this place? Arthur, did you see the post office?

Arthur. It said Laurenceville.

Ma. Hhn. School kinda. Nice. I wonder what that big yellow house set back was.—Now it's beginning to be Trenton.

Caroline. Papa, it was near here that George Washington crossed the Delaware. It was near Trenton, Mama. He was first in war and first in peace, and first in the hearts of his countrymen.

Ma. (*Surveying the passing world, serene and didactic*) Well, the thing I like about him best was that he never told a lie. (*The children are duly cast down. There is a pause.* Arthur *stands up and looks at the car ahead.*) There's a sunset for you. There's nothing like a good sunset.

Arthur. There's an Ohio license in front of us. Ma, have you ever been to Ohio?

Ma. No.

(*A dreamy silence descends upon them.* Caroline *sits closer to her father, towards the left;* Arthur *closer to* Ma *on the right, who puts her arm around him, unsentimentally.*)

Arthur. Ma, what a lotta people there are in the world, Ma. There must be thousands and thousands in the United States. Ma, how many are there?

Ma. I don't know. Ask your father.

Arthur. Pa, how many are there?

Elmer. There are a hundred and twenty-six million, Kate.

Ma. (*Giving a pressure about* Arthur's *shoulder*) And they all like to drive out in the evening with their children beside 'm. Why doesn't somebody sing something? Arthur, you're always singing something; what's the matter with you?

Arthur. All right. What'll we sing? (*He sketches:*)

> "In the Blue Ridge Mountains of Virginia,
>   On the . . ."

No, I don't like that any more. Let's do:

> "I been workin' on de railroad
>   (Caroline *joins in.*)
>   All de liblong day.
>   (Ma *sings.*)
>   I been workin' on de railroad
>   (Elmer *joins in.*)
>   Just to pass de time away.
>   Don't you hear de whistle blowin',' " etc.

(Ma *suddenly jumps up with a wild cry and a large circular gesture.*)

Ma. Elmer, that signpost said Camden. I saw it.

Elmer. All right, Kate, if you're sure.

(*Much shifting of gears, backing, and jolting*)

Ma. Yes, there it is. Camden—five miles. Dear old Beulah. (*The journey continues.*) Now, children, you be good and quiet during dinner. She's just got out of bed after a big sorta operation, and we must all move around kinda quiet. First you drop me and Caroline at the door and just say hello, and then you men-folk go over to the Y.M.C.A. and come back for dinner in about an hour.

Caroline. (*Shutting her eyes and pressing her fists passion-*

ately against her nose) I see the first star. Everybody make a wish.

> "Star light, star bright,
> First star I seen tonight.
> I wish I may, I wish I might
> Have the wish I wish tonight."

(*Then solemnly*)   Pins. Mama, you say "needles."
(*She interlocks little fingers with her mother across back of seat.*)

Ma. Needles.

Caroline. Shakespeare. Ma, you say "Longfellow."

Ma. Longfellow.

Caroline. Now it's a secret and I can't tell it to anybody. Ma, you make a wish.

Ma. (*With almost grim humor*) No, I can make wishes without waiting for no star. And I can tell my wishes right out loud too. Do you want to hear them?

Caroline. (*Resignedly*) No, Ma, we know 'm already. We've heard 'm. (*She hangs her head affectedly on her left shoulder and says with unmalicious mimicry:*) You want me to be a good girl and you want Arthur to be honest-in-word-and-deed.

Ma. (*Majestically*) Yes. So mind yourself.

Elmer. Caroline, take out that letter from Beulah in my coat pocket by you and read aloud the places I marked with red pencil.

Caroline. (*Laboriously making it out*) "*A few blocks after you pass the two big oil tanks on your left . . .*"

Everybody. (*Pointing backward*) There they are!

Caroline. " *. . . you come to a corner where there's an A and P store on the left and a firehouse kittycorner to it. . . .*"

(*They all jubilantly identify these landmarks.*) ". . . turn
right, go two blocks, and our house is Weyerhauser St.,
Number 471.*"

Ma.   It's an even nicer street than they used to live on.
And right handy to an A and P.

Caroline.   (*Whispering*) Ma, it's better than our street.
It's richer than our street. Ma, isn't Beulah richer than
we are?

Ma.   (*Looking at her with a firm and glassy eye*) Mind
yourself, Missy. I don't want to hear anybody talking
about rich or not rich when I'm around. If people
aren't nice I don't care how rich they are. I live in the
best street in the world because my husband and
children live there. (*She glares impressively at* Caroline *a
moment to let this lesson sink in, then looks up, sees* Beulah *off
left and waves.*) There's Beulah standing on the steps
lookin' for us.

(Beulah *enters from left, also waving. They all call out:*
"*Hello, Beulah—hello.*"   *Presently they are all getting
out of the car, except* Elmer, *busy with brakes.*)

Beulah.   Hello, Mama. Well, lookit how Arthur and
Caroline are growing.

Ma.   They're bursting all their clothes.

Beulah.   (*Crossing in front of them and kissing her father
long and affectionately*) Hello, Papa. Good old papa.
You look tired, Pa.

Ma.   Yes, your pa needs a rest. Thank Heaven, his
vacation has come just now. We'll feed him up and
let him sleep late. (Elmer *gets out of car and stands in
front of it.*) Pa has a present for you, Loolie. He would
go and buy it.

Beulah.   Why, Pa, you're terrible to go and buy anything
for me. Isn't he terrible?

(The Stage Manager *removes the automobile*.)

Ma. Well, it's a secret. You can open it at dinner.

Beulah. (*Puts her arm around his neck and rubs her nose against his temple*) Crazy old pa, goin' buyin' things! It's me that ought to be buyin' things for you, Pa.

Elmer. Oh, no! There's only one Loolie in the world.

Beulah. (*Whispering, as her eyes fill with tears*) Are you glad I'm still alive, Pa? (*She kisses him abruptly and goes back to the house steps*.)

Elmer. Where's Horace, Loolie?

Beulah. He was kep' over a little at the office. He'll be here any minute. He's crazy to see you all.

Ma. All right. You men go over to the Y and come back in about an hour.

Beulah. Go straight along, Pa, you can't miss it. It just stares at yuh. (Elmer *and* Arthur *exit down right*.) Well, come on upstairs, Ma, and take your things.— Caroline, there's a surprise for you in the back yard.

Caroline. Rabbits?

Beulah. No.

Caroline. Chickins?

Beulah. No. Go and see. (Caroline *runs off stage, down left*.) There are two new puppies. You be thinking over whether you can keep one in Newark.

Ma. I guess we can. (Ma *and* Beulah *turn and walk way up stage right. The Stage Manager pushes out a cot from the left, and places it down left on a slant so that its foot is towards the left*. Beulah *and* Ma *come down stage center towards left*.) It's a nice house, Beulah. You just got a *lovely* home.

Beulah. When I got back from the hospital, Horace

had moved everything into it, and there wasn't anything for me to do.

Ma.   It's lovely.

(Beulah *sits on the cot, testing the springs.*)

Beulah.   I think you'll find this comfortable, Ma.

(Beulah *sits on down stage end of it.*)

Ma.   (*Taking off her hat*) Oh, I could sleep on a heapa
shoes, Loolie! I don't have no trouble sleepin'. (*She
sits down, up stage of her.*) Now let me look at my girl.
Well, well, when I last saw you, you didn't know me.
You kep' saying: *When's Mama comin'? When's Mama
comin'?* But the doctor sent me away.

Beulah.   (*Puts her head on her mother's shoulder and
weeps*) It was awful, Mama. It was awful. She didn't
even live a few minutes, Mama. It was awful.

Ma.   (*In a quick, light, urgent undertone*) God thought
best, dear. God thought best. We don't understand
why. We just go on, honey, doin' our business. (*Then
almost abruptly*) Well, now, (*Stands up*) what are we
giving the men to eat tonight?

Beulah.   There's a chicken in the oven.

Ma.   What time didya put it in?

Beulah.   (*Restraining her*) Aw, Ma, don't go yet. (*Taking
her mother's hand and drawing her down beside her*)
I like to sit here with you this way. You always get the
fidgets when we try and pet yuh, Mama.

Ma.   (*Ruefully, laughing*) Yes, it's kinda foolish. I'm
just an old Newark bag-a-bones. (*She glances at the
backs of her hands.*)

Beulah.   (*Indignantly*) Why, Ma, you're good-lookin'!
We always said you were good-lookin'.—And besides,
you're the best ma we could ever have.

Ma. (*Uncomfortable*) Well, I hope you like me. There's nothin' like bein' liked by your family.—(*Rises*) Now I'm going downstairs to look at the chicken. You stretch out here for a minute and shut your eyes. (*She helps* Beulah *to a lying position.*) Have you got everything laid in for breakfast before the shops close?

Beulah. Oh, you know! Ham and eggs.

(*They both laugh.* Ma *puts an imaginary blanket over* Beulah.)

Ma. I declare I never could understand what men see in ham and eggs. I think they're horrible.—What time did you put the chicken in?

Beulah. Five o'clock.

Ma. Well, now, you shut your eyes for ten minutes.

(Ma *turns, walks directly up stage, then along the back wall to the right as she absent-mindedly and indistinctly sings:*)

"There were ninety and nine that safely lay
In the shelter of the fold . . ."

AND THE CURTAIN FALLS

The Patchwork Quilt

A FANTASY IN ONE ACT

by RACHEL LYMAN FIELD

CHARACTERS

Old Mrs. Willis
Anne Wendall, *her daughter*
Joe Wendall, *Anne's husband*
Betty, *their daughter*

In the Fantasy

Molly
William
Emily

THE PATCHWORK QUILT

SCENE:

An upstairs bedroom and sitting room combined, of a modern city house, which has been 'done over' recently. The mahogany furniture somehow fails to give the impression of antiquity that the decorator probably intended. We know at a glance that none of it has been much lived upon, and the conventional angles at which the chairs are arranged accentuate this feeling of newness. Several good prints, in subdued tones, hang on the walls, but the only picture which seems to be a personal belonging is a portrait in an oval gold frame over the fireplace. This is the likeness, in an old-fashioned pastel, of a little girl of six, round-eyed and serious, with the smooth ringlets and low-necked dress of forty years ago. A coal-fire burns in the grate. It is late afternoon.

When the curtain rises, old Mrs. Willis *is wandering aimlessly about the room. She goes from one article of furniture to another, fingering each carefully, and then moving on to another as if she were searching for something that should feel familiar to her fingers. She is a frail old lady in obviously new and handsome black clothes, in which she seems tiny and out of place. Over her face there is a film of daze and bewilderment.*

She has reached the bed, and is fingering a grey silk puff lying there, turning it over and over with obvious disappointment, when Joe Wendall, *and his wife,* Anne, *enter. The former is in his forties, well dressed, with a stubborn chin and the keen practical face of a businessman. The woman is rather pretty in a nervous, twentieth-century sort of way. She wears a smart afternoon dress, and is removing her hat and gloves as she enters.*

55

Anne. (*To her husband, indicating* Mrs. Willis) There, Joe, you can see for yourself the state she's in! (*Going to the old lady*) Oh, Mother, do sit down, and don't keep fidgeting so! (*Old* Mrs. Willis *looks at her in bewilderment. She makes no answer, and her daughter speaks again, more loudly this time, though with an effort at kindness.*) What are you looking for?

Mrs. Willis. (*Turning from one to the other blankly*) I'm very sorry to disturb you, but I'm looking for my room. I seem to have lost the way.

Anne. (*To* Joe) Just as I told you. This is one of her bad days! (*Speaking in loud, simple tones as if to a child*) Why, this is your room, Mother, you've just forgotten again. . . .

Mrs. Willis. (*Polite but firm*) Oh, no, I wouldn't have forgotten my own room, not after so many years—such a pretty one, too, with a table and six carved chairs. (*Proudly*) They came from Boston—and a beautiful patchwork quilt.

Joe. (*With irritation*) Can't you stop her, Anne? It's hopeless once she gets started on that old quilt.

Mrs. Willis. (*Nodding to herself*) There's not another one like it anywheres round. I always said the rainbow itself wasn't a mite prettier'n my patchwork quilt.

Anne. Oh, Mother you're all mixed up again—you're in your room at my house. (*Leading her over to a chair*) Now, you sit down here by the fire, and try very hard to listen to what Joe and I ask you.

Mrs. Willis. (*Feeling the chair*) This chair isn't mine! It's got plain legs—mine had carved ones—

Joe. (*Helping* Anne *out*) What's the matter with these chairs? I think Anne's fixed you up a real pretty room.

Mrs. Willis. (*Blankly*) Anne—Anne isn't here any

more. (*She looks plaintively from one to the other.*) I can't just remember what happened, but she isn't here any more. Emily's all I've got now.

Anne. (*To* Joe) You see, she doesn't even know me!

Joe. (*Shortly*) Must be a real cheerful feeling!

Anne. Don't, Joe. I'm worried enough with this business about the farm.

Mrs. Willis. (*Repeating wistfully*) Yes, Emily's all I've got now—(*She points to the picture over the mantle.*)

Anne. (*Turning again to her, and speaking wearily*) Why, Mother, don't you remember that Emily's dead? (*Leaning over her and speaking distinctly*) She's been dead for over forty years.

Mrs. Willis. (*Trembling a little*) Emily—dead? Why, she couldn't be. She comes to see me real often—she's the only one of my children that does now—

Anne. (*To* Joe) You can see how she's failed the last month, Joe.

Joe. Yes, don't see how we'll get anything out of her in time.

Anne. (*To* Joe) Just leave her to herself for a few minutes: it may bring her round.

(*They move away from the old lady, who sits in her chair by the fire, staring straight before her, and occasionally feeling the chair legs hopefully, to sink back again disappointed at their plain surfaces.*)

Joe. (*Turning to* Anne *with an air of finality*) Look here, Anne, are you sure that deed isn't with her things somewhere?

Anne. (*Impatiently*) Of course it isn't, Joe, you know I went through everything when we had the room done over.

Joe. Still, I always said you made a mistake clearing out all her junk wholesale like that. We might—

Anne. (*Interrupting*) You know I couldn't have stood those old moth-eaten things another day! It wasn't as if the furniture had been really good, either—that ghastly walnut and horsehair and a patchwork quilt with all the colors of the rainbow swearing at each other! (*On the defensive*) And I didn't send everything away—there's Emily's picture—the decorator said it had nice coloring.

Joe. (*Worried*) Well, I don't give a darn what the fool decorator said, it's that deed I'm after, and we've got to find out where she keeps it.

Anne. But, Joe, they must have a record at Green River.

Joe. (*Pulling out an envelope*) Heard this morning—seems things got all mixed up there after the town hall burned down. A lot of the old books and records were lost, and it's going to take months to straighten out all the boundaries and claims. It may not even have been registered. They thought, of course, that we had the deed to Mother's place. In that case it would be easy enough.

Anne. Well, but didn't you explain it to Mr. Jenkins?

Joe. Of course I did! But you know what he is—says he'll take Mother's place at our price, house, woodland, and all if the title's clear and the sale can go right through.

Anne. But he'll give us a few days more surely?

Joe. Not Jenkins. He's made up his mind to start right in on the hotel plans—unless the ground's broken before frost sets in all the building will have to wait till next year, and he says that rather than do that he'll take the Thompson place five miles north, though the view doesn't compare with ours.

Anne. (*Eagerly*) We could let him start in work right away and get the deed later.

Joe. (*Flinging out his hands with an irritated gesture*) But can't you see, Anne, legally we don't own that place. Of course everybody knows the farm belongs to your mother, but we can't prove it without that blamed piece of paper!

Anne. (*Earnestly*) Oh, Joe, we've got to put that sale through somehow! Why, think what it would mean to us—

Joe. (*Gloomily*) Do you suppose I've been thinking of anything else all week? If he takes the Thompson place, everybody'll buy at that end of the town and our land will go way down in value.

Anne. We must find that deed! Think of all we could do with the money the place would bring. We could buy that stucco house in Wildwood Park that you said we couldn't afford, and go abroad for next summer, and get a Cadillac instead of the Ford coupé.

Joe. Say, Anne, if you'd get her talking instead of spending money maybe we won't ever get hold of—

Anne. All right, I'll try again— (*With a little sigh*) and we could have a French governess for Betty just like the Lawrences', or maybe that new boarding school would be better. . . .

Joe. Oh, Betty's all right. Funny, the way she and your mother seem to hit it off.

Anne. But, Joe, I don't think it's good for her to see anyone whose mind wanders so. (*Going towards* Mrs. Willis, *who is sitting just where they left her, staring bef re her in a subdued, unhappy way*) Now, Mother, we want you to try and remember about the farm.

Mrs. Willis. (*Rousing for the first time at the last word*) The farm—yes—you have to climb the hill to get there, right on top it is. There's lilacs by the door, and you can look out over four counties from the front porch.

Joe. (*Encouraged*) There, she does remember. (*To* Mrs. Willis) Now about the deed, you must have had one. You know, a paper that says the farm belongs to you.

Mrs. Willis. (*Reminiscently*) White lilacs, they are—

Anne. (*Urging*) The deed, Mother, try to remember where it is.

Mrs. Willis. (*Her face wrinkling with the effort to remember*) I don't know—everything's got all tangled up in my head, like a ball o' yarn—

Joe. (*Speaking slowly and distinctly*) Listen to me, Mother—a little piece of paper with a red seal—that's what we want. And it says that the farm and woodland belong to you—you must have put it somewhere?

Mrs. Willis. (*Now hopelessly bewildered*) Maybe if Emily would come she'd tell you what you want to know— but you said she's—she's— (*Her voice trails away plaintively.*)

Anne. (*Trying to draw her out*) You told me once that Father gave it to you on your wedding day—don't you remember?

Mrs. Willis. (*Feeling of the chair, and rising to go to the table*) I want my carved chairs, and my table with the scratches on it. (*Smiling to herself at some remembrance of her own*) Anne, she always would smuggle her kitten to meals with her—that's how the scratches come to be there. I like to sit and feel them when I'm all alone.

Anne. (*Turning to* Joe) It's no use when she gets all worked up like this.

Mrs. Willis. (*By the bed, her voice rising in agitation*) It isn't here—someone's taken my quilt!

Joe. (*To* Anne) Good Lord, she's started on that again! Well, I guess it isn't much use, and I've got to let Jenkins know by tonight.

Anne. She may quiet down if we leave her here awhile. Sometimes she acts quite like herself.

Joe. (*With a shrug*) All right, I'll take another look through those papers we kept from her desk—might give me a clue.

Anne. (*To* Mrs. Willis) Sit down again, Mother. (*Helping her to the chair again*) That's better, now you'll try and remember about the paper—folded up small with sealing wax on it. Joe and I'll come back soon.

Mrs. Willis. (*Wearily*) I'll try—but if I could have my chairs and my quilt—

Anne. (*To* Joe *at the door*) You fixed it all up with the lawyer so her signature won't be necessary?

Joe. Yes, she's not really responsible any more, and it's lucky in this case, for she'd never let the old place go, not the way she hangs on to things.

Anne. That sale simply must go through, Joe.

(*They go out, and* Mrs. Willis *stares after them wonderingly.*)

Mrs. Willis. (*Shaking her head*) Those people wanted something—something they thought I had. (*Wistfully*) I don't know what it's all about. (*She begins to whimper a little brokenly to herself.*) They're all gone, and I've looked everywhere for 'em—my carved chairs, and my patchwork quilt, and Emily's gone, too—

(*She cries softly in the slowly darkening room. Twilight is coming, and save for the firelight the room seems stiff and cheerless. Suddenly the door bursts open, and a merry little girl of six or seven bounds in, her arms filled with an old patchwork quilt whose folds trail after her. She runs towards the old lady eagerly.*)

Betty.   Look what I found, Grandma!

(Mrs. Willis *turns, rising with incredulous joy at sight of the quilt.*)

Mrs. Willis.   (*Trembling a little*)   Then it isn't lost— Betty, you've brought Grandma's patchwork quilt back to her—

Betty.   But it was on Katy the cook's bed.

Mrs. Willis.   (*Gathering the quilt in her arms, pressing its familiar folds close*)   My patchwork quilt—mine— mine—

Betty.   It's got so many colors in it, not just one like the kind Mother buys, (*Fingering it with interest*) and it's pretty.

Mrs. Willis.   (*Softly*)   It's beautiful.

Betty.   (*Wonderingly*)   You're crying on it.

Mrs. Willis.   (*In soft, sure tones, the dazed look beginning to slip from her face*)   It's all coming back to me now.

Betty.   (*Curiously*)   What's coming back, Grandma? (*Bending over the quilt*) I don't see anything.

(Mrs. Willis *moves to the chair by the fire, sinking into it contentedly and spreading the gay maze of color over her knees. The firelight falls warmly on the little squares, as she fingers them with the eager greeting reserved only for old friends.*)

Mrs. Willis. There's that blue piece that came from Mother's old winter cashmere—she always got it out come the first of November and wore it till March, excepting her best black on Sundays and her second best for afternoons.

Betty. (*Bending over to see*) Which one, Grandma?

Mrs. Willis. (*Finding another*) And this is from my first party dress.

Betty. (*In surprise*) Why, Grandma, did you go to parties, real ones?

Mrs. Willis. (*Nodding*) Never missed one— A green silk this dress was, with a black sash and white tatting collar. William always liked me in green—

Betty. Who was William?

Mrs. Willis. (*Tenderly*) William was your grandfather. (*Suddenly she goes on speaking with a kind of slow revelation.*) Why, every one of them is bringing me back something— a day, or the folks I knew and have been wanting— (*Lifting up her head triumphantly*) Things are getting just as clear, nothing's mixed up any more now I've got back my quilt!

Betty. (*Who has been examining it*) Here's a pretty square with pink flowers on it!

Mrs. Willis. (*Pleased*) Well, I declare, if I hadn't clean forgotten that! 'Twas a bit of ribbon Great-Aunt Dolly brought me clear from Paris.

Betty. I've got a hat that came from Paris—it tickles my ears.

Mrs. Willis. I had a time piecin' that square to fit, but the ribbon's hardly frayed a mite.

Betty. And here's a little yellow one—what was that, Grandma?

Mrs. Willis. (*Touching it fondly*) That was a piece from Emily's best dress.

Betty. (*Surprised*) Aunt Emily in the picture up there? (*Pointing to it*)

Mrs. Willis. Yes, she had it on in that picture, only it didn't show as much as she hoped it would. (*Reminiscently*) William bought that dress for her in Portland the day she was six— 'twas all handmade and very dear. I scolded him for paying so much, but he could never do enough for Emily.

Betty. (*Studying the picture*) And did Aunt Emily like it?

Mrs. Willis. She couldn't wait every afternoon till I'd get through my work, so I could dress her in it and curl her hair. Then she'd sit down in her little chair side of me while I did my sewing. (*Thoughtfully*) Making this very quilt I was then. (*After a moment's pause she goes on as if she were seeing it all over again.*) Sometimes I'd baste on a square and let her sew it. She thought she was a real, grown-up lady then, and she was just as proud—

Betty. (*Eagerly*) Oh, I want to see the ones Aunt Emily sewed—which ones, Grandma?

Mrs. Willis. (*Thoughtfully*) Let me see—about halfway through I was, and her stitches were pretty big and crooked, but I never did have the heart to rip them out.

Betty. (*Excitedly*) There! All round that big white piece in the middle—look, they're just as wobbly, like mountains and valleys in my geography.

Mrs. Willis. (*With a little gasp*) The white square in the middle, yes— (*Rubbing her forehead thoughtfully*) There was something about it. It meant more than the others, that's why I let Emily sew it— (*Her voice trails off softly.*) Something about the white piece that made me happy.

(*She sits smoothing the white square, when a voice outside calls "Betty! Betty!" The child rises and starts towards the door.*)

Betty. I've got to go to supper now, Grandma, but I'll come back when you've remembered all about the white one—

Mrs. Willis. (*Repeating softly*) The white one—

(*She bends over and kisses it as if it were alive. Suddenly from the dimness of the room a figure appears. As the firelight falls on it, we see it is a lovely young girl, wearing a heavy white satin dress in the style of fifty years ago. Her face is flower-like, just what old Mrs. Willis' might have been at twenty. Over her hair is a draping of old lace. At sight of her Mrs. Willis leans forward in her chair, speaking with soft wonder.*)

Mrs. Willis. My wedding dress—and why, why, I couldn't have looked as pretty as all that!

(*The girl looks about her, then beckons eagerly to someone behind her, speaking in happy, excited tones.*)

Girl. It's all right, William, there's no one here.

(*Another figure steps out of the shadows, a straight, boyish one this time, clad in the tight grey trousers and neat black braid-trimmed coat of the period. His eyes are luminous with suppressed emotions, and his face pale. In his hands he carries a bouquet of white lilacs tied with a long shimmering ribbon. At sight of him old Mrs. Willis gives a little cry, and holds out her arms to him, but neither he nor the girl is aware of her presence, being completely absorbed in each other.*)

William. (*Eagerly*) Molly, I thought they'd never let me see you—

Molly. I know—sister said she never saw a bridegroom behave the way you do, but I don't care, there never was one like you, anyway, and I wanted to see you, too, before— (*Catching at his sleeve*) I've been worrying so, thinking about all the things that might happen— how you *might* forget the flowers, or the ring *might* fall out of your pocket and you not know till the minister asked for it—and how could we ever be married then?

William. (*Touching his pocket*) It's all safe, and I didn't forget the flowers— (*He holds out the lilacs, and she takes them with a little cry—burying her face in them.*)

Molly. Oh, William, I knew you'd remember about the lilacs—Mother thought you'd bring lilies of the valley, but I knew better— And these came from the old Todd place I know, because they're sweeter and whiter than any others. (*Shyly*) Or maybe I just think so because it was up there that we—that you said—

William. (*Bending over her*) What I'm saying now and every minute of the day—that I love you—I love you, Molly. (*There is a pause for a moment as she slips into his arms. Then he goes on softly.*) I was up before light this morning, I couldn't sleep for knowing what day it was, so I went up the hill to the old Todd place to pick these before they opened too far. The bush was full of them, all nodding away in the wind, and when I came up close a thrush flew right up out of it and began to sing, just as if it knew—

Molly. (*Softly*) About us? I wouldn't wonder . . . that old lilac-bush must have heard you last fall when you asked me. (*Touching the flowers fondly*) Maybe these very flowers were listening—maybe they hoped they'd come to our wedding!

William. (*A little awkwardly*) You look sort of like them today, Molly—I—I'm glad they let me see you first, before the others. You didn't mind?

Molly. I wanted you to, (*Smoothing her dress*) and I'm glad you think it's pretty—wasn't it good of Aunt Dolly to give it to me? It isn't every bride has a satin that can stand alone!

William. (*Smiling at her*) But I don't want it to stand alone—I want you to be in it!

Molly. (*Listening*) There goes the knocker! Oh, William, they're beginning to come!

William. (*Earnestly*) Molly, maybe you thought it was queer I didn't give you a ring to wear before now—

Molly. (*Simply*) I didn't need to have a ring to know you loved me.

William. But I've brought you something, Molly, you can't wear it, but I wanted you to have it before we're married, something you're to keep for always.

(*He fumbles in his pocket and draws out a thin, folded paper with a seal.*)

Molly. (*Excitedly*) Oh, William, what is it? It's too dark in here to read—what does it say?

William. It says that the old Todd place is going to have a new owner—it's going to be yours from now on.

Molly. Mine—mine—oh, William! (*She buries her head against his coat, and he pats her hair tenderly, lifting up her face gently.*)

William. There, I've gone and mussed your hair, and your sister'll scold me, for I promised her not to touch you.

Molly. (*Smiling up at him radiantly*) Is it really mine—for always?

William. For always.

(*At this, old* Mrs. Willis *cannot contain herself any longer, and she leans forward in her chair, speaking to him earnestly.*)

Mrs. Willis. And I've never let anyone else have it, William, I've always tried— (*But neither of them hears the old lady.*)

(Molly *takes the paper and kisses it, then she tucks it into the satin bodice of her dress, hiding it safely away out of sight.*)

Molly. (*Turning with a smile to* William) There, I can wear it, William! All the time the minister is marrying us I'll feel it lying there, and it'll be just as if I were wearing the house and the lilac-bushes and the view of the four counties—only no one will know except you and me!

William. We'll know, dear.

Molly. And I think I shall always keep it wrapped up in my wedding satin, even when I'm too old to wear it any more.

William. (*Listening*) I can hear them talking downstairs. It must be nearly time—

Molly. (*Suddenly clinging to him*) Oh, William, hold me close, never mind if you do rumple me—I'm afraid.

William. Afraid, why, dear?

Molly. I don't know, I just am—sometimes—you know —it's all the things that may be going to happen to us and our house—

William. (*Gently correcting her*) *Your* house, dear.

Molly. But I'll be growing old, dear, some time. I woke up in the night thinking about it, and I felt cold and afraid, and you weren't there to tell me everything was all right.

William. (*Comfortingly*) I'm here now, and everything is all right—we're going to be married. Come, they're calling you.

Molly. (*Touching the bodice of her dress*) It's here, William—it's all safe and warm—

(*They fade into the gloom again, leaving old* Mrs. Willis *alone by the fire, the quilt still over her knees. She looks at the place where the two have stood with an expression of longing, and, stretching out her arms, whispers.*)

Mrs. Willis. Oh, William, say it again—say everything's all right—I'm here all alone—

(*Then she bends over the quilt again, fingering the square in the center. The fire flares up a little, and other figures approach her. This time it is an older* Molly, *a serene and beautiful young woman of twenty-seven, wearing a full dress of figured green material. Her face is more thoughtful, and her hair is worn in a smooth, forgotten fashion. She carries a great bag of sewing on her arm, and leads along a tiny child—a little girl with round, serious eyes and smooth ringlets, exactly like the child in the portrait. Her quaint, low-necked dress is buttercup yellow, and she wears it with childish satisfaction.*)

Mrs. Willis. (*Half rising from her chair and stretching out her arms with a low cry*) Emily!

(*The two settle themselves near the fire.* Emily *on a low footstool by her mother's chair*)

Molly. Come, dear, let's sit up close to the fire.

Emily. Does the fire like to see me in my yellow dress?

Molly. (*Smiling*) Not as much as Father does.

Emily. (*Chuckling*) No, because the fire sticks out red tongues at me, and Father doesn't—he always kisses me.

Molly. Then I must sew ever so many squares before he gets home, so he will kiss me too!

(*She takes out some patchwork squares stitched together, and begins to sew.* Emily *watches her intently.*)

Emily. Why are your eyes all shiny, Mother, just like before a party?

Molly. (*Patting the square she is at work on*) Because I've come to the center of my quilt—see.

Emily. (*Touching it*) What a funny big white square! Why isn't it pretty like the other ones?

Molly. I love it more than all the rest.

Emily. I like the colored ones better. Why don't you?

Molly. Because— (*Smiling to herself*) it was a piece of the dress I wore when Father and I were married.

Emily. (*Eagerly*) Was I there?

Molly. (*Smiling at her tenderly*) No, dear, I didn't know you then.

Emily. (*Wonderingly*) Didn't you? I've always known you. (*After a pause*) I wish I had been there. What makes you put the white patch in the middle?

Molly. Because the patch I love best must go there, and— (*Smiling mysteriously*) there's a secret about it.

Emily. Does Father know the secret too?

Molly. Yes, and some time I'll tell you—when you're grown up.

Emily. (*Disappointed*) But that's a long way off.

Molly. (*With vague dread*) A long, long way off, dear.

Emily. Let's call the white patch Best-of-all because it's got a secret.

Molly. Yes, we will, and we'll remember how precious it is—that's why no one must ever have the quilt except Mother.

Emily. What does the secret look like?

Molly. (*Smiling*) You see it every day whenever you run around the house or pick me lilacs in the spring, or look out over the hills to the four counties.

Emily. (*In surprise*) My, not all that in such a little square? (*She bends over it curiously.*)

Molly. (*Happily*) Yes, it's all there, but only Father and I know—

Emily. And me—only I can't see any house or hills or anything—

Molly. (*Kissing her*) Some day you will, darling, and you'll love it just as Mother does.

Emily. I want to sew on the secret patch.

Molly. (*Hesitating*) Well—perhaps—I was going to do it myself because we must be very careful—it's such a precious one.

Emily. I'll be just as careful and take the littlest stitches.

Molly. (*Putting it in her hands*) There, in and out, where I've basted it, and be sure to pull the thread tight every time so there won't be a single loose stitch. (*Emily sets to work seriously, and with a will. As her fingers touch the satin, she hears something and puts her ear close to the square to listen.*)

Emily. Why—it *crackles!* Is that what makes it so precious, Mother?

Molly. Yes, dear.

Emily. (*Seriously*) Well, I think the white patch would like me to be wearing your gold thimble.

Molly. (*Slipping it from her finger to the child's with a smile*) Here it is then, but be careful.

Emily. I will—and won't Father be surprised to see me sewing just like a real grown-up lady?

Molly. I think I hear him now stamping the snow off his boots at the back door. I'll go and tell him to come in and see who's making a call!

(Emily *chuckles joyously at this, and sews very hard, while* Molly *rises and slips away. Old* Mrs. Willis *leans forward, stretching out her arms to the child appealingly. Then* Emily *too slips off into the gloom. At the same moment voices sound near by, and presently the electric lights are turned on, revealing* Anne *and* Joe. *The sudden light dazzles old* Mrs. Willis, *and she sits still with the quilt spread all about her, a mass of jumbled color.*)

Anne. (*With an exclamation of annoyance*) Oh, that dreadful quilt! I thought I'd seen the last of it! Where in the world was that unearthed?

(*At this moment* Betty *enters, running past her parents, and throwing herself eagerly on her grandmother and the quilt.*)

Betty. Oh, Grandma, I've got just five minutes before I have to go to bed, and you said you'd tell me about the white square!

Mrs. Willis. (*Stroking it*) It—it's very precious, and it's a secret—

Anne. (*Intervening*) Betty, you must go right to your room. Don't ask Grandma a single question.

Betty. Just about the quilt, Mother?

Anne. (*Touching it*) No, and I'm sure I don't know where you found it.

Betty. (*Hurriedly*) It was in Katy's room, but I wanted it on my bed. It's pretty and Grandma made it, and there's one patch that came from Paris.

Anne. No, dear, you must take this right back to Katy's room. You have a nice pink one for your bed.

Mrs. Willis. (*Nervously rousing herself*) You won't take my quilt away. I've been wanting it for a long time.

Betty. Just let Grandma tell me about this one, Mother? (*Pointing to the white patch in the middle*)

Joe. (*Firmly*) No, Betty, take it away now. Mother and I want to talk to Grandma.

(Anne *gathers it quickly out of old* Mrs. Willis' *clinging fingers, piling it into the child's arms.*)

Mrs. Willis. (*Protesting weakly*) It's my quilt, Anne, and I want it, won't you let me keep it? There isn't another one like it anywhere—

Anne. Why, Mother, I couldn't think of such a thing, not after the cook's had it on her bed, and when you've got such a pretty grey one! Here, Betty, take it to Katy and then go to bed.

(Betty *moves towards the door reluctantly, the quilt in her arms. Old* Mrs. Willis *rises once, trying to make a last effort to rescue the quilt, and giving a last little despairing gasp of protest. But* Anne *leads her firmly back to the chair by the fire.* Betty *pauses by the door, fingering the white square. As she does so she gives a surprised start, putting her ear down close to it.*)

Betty. Why—it *crackles!*

(Anne *waves her off, closing the door on the child and the quilt.* Joe *has already started on the old subject.*)

Joe. Have you been trying to remember, Mother, about the deed of the old place?

Mrs. Willis. (*Plaintively*) Every square was a piece out of the past to me, and you won't let me have it.

Anne. Now listen to Joe, Mother. It's just one little thing we want.

Joe. Try to think—the paper they gave you the day you were married.

Mrs. Willis. (*Looks from one to the other blankly; the film of daze has begun to spread over her face again, and she murmurs vaguely.*) The white square in the center—I liked it the best—I don't remember why—(*Her voice trails off incoherently.*)

(*After a moment's uncertainty the old lady rises and resumes her occupation of roaming from one piece of furniture to another, feeling the chair legs and the table top.*)

Anne. (*To* Joe) It's absolutely no use, Joe: Not when she starts on that quilt.

Joe. (*Gloomily*) Well, I guess we'll have that old place on our hands till we're a hundred!

(*The two go out, and old* Mrs. Willis *moves patiently about from one thing to another as she did at the beginning of the play. At last she reaches the bed, where she bends down to finger the grey silk puff.*)

Mrs. Willis. (*To herself*) It's all grey now.

(*She shakes her head a little wearily, and stares straight before her.*)

CURTAIN

The Valiant

by

HOLWORTHY HALL

and

ROBERT MIDDLEMASS

CHARACTERS

Warden Holt, *about* 60
Father Daly, *the prison chaplain*
James Dyke, *the Prisoner*
Josephine Paris, *the Girl, about* 18
Dan, *a Jailer*
An Attendant

SCENE: *The Warden's office in the State's Prison at Wethersfield, Connecticut.*

TIME: *About half-past eleven on a rainy night.*

THE VALIANT

The curtain rises upon the Warden's *office in the State's Prison at Wethersfield, Connecticut. It is a large, cold, unfriendly apartment, with bare floors and staring, white-washed walls; it is furnished only with the* Warden's *flat-topped desk, and swivel chair, with a few straight-backed chairs, one beside the desk and others against the walls, with a water-cooler and an eight-day clock. On the* Warden's *desk are a telephone instrument, a row of electric push buttons, and a bundle of forty or fifty letters. At the back of the room are two large windows, crossed with heavy bars; at the left there is a door to an anteroom, and at the right there are two doors, of which the more distant leads to the office of the deputy warden, and the nearer is seldom used.*

Warden Holt, *dressed in a dark brown sack suit, with a negligee shirt and black string tie, carelessly knotted in a bow, is seated at his desk, reflectively smoking a long, thin cigar. He is verging toward sixty, and his responsibilities have printed themselves in italics upon his countenance. His brown hair, and bushy eyebrows are heavily shot with gray; there is a deep parenthesis of wrinkles at the corners of his mouth and innumerable fine lines about his eyes. His bearing indicates that he is accustomed to rank as a despot, and yet his expression is far from that of an unreasoning tyrant. He is no sentimentalist, but he believes that in each of us there is a constant oscillation of good and evil; and that all evil should be justly punished in this world, and that all good should be generously rewarded— in the next.*

Behind the Warden, *the prison chaplain stands at one of the barred windows, gazing steadily out into the night.* Father Daly *is a slender, white-haired priest of somewhat more than middle age; he is dressed in slightly shabby clericals. His face is calm, intellectual, and inspiring; but just at this moment, it gives evidence of a peculiar depression.*

The Warden *blows a cloud of smoke to the ceiling, inspects the cigar critically, drums on the desk, and finally peers over his shoulder at the chaplain. He clears his throat and speaks brusquely.*

The Warden. Has it started to rain?

Father Daly. (*Answers without turning*) Yes, it has.

The Warden. (*Glaring at his cigar and impatiently tossing it aside*) It *would* rain tonight. (*His tone is vaguely resentful, as though the weather had added a needless fraction to his impatience.*)

Father Daly. (*Glances at a big silver watch*) It's past eleven o'clock. (*He draws a deep breath and comes slowly to the center of the room.*) We haven't much longer to wait.

The Warden. No, thank God! (*He gets up, and goes to the water-cooler; with the glass halfway to his lips he pauses.*) Was he quiet when you left him?

Father Daly. (*A trifle abstractedly*) Yes, yes, he was perfectly calm and I believe he'll stay so to the very end.

The Warden. (*Finishes his drink, comes back to his desk and lights a fresh cigar*) You've got to hand it to him, Father; I never saw such nerve in all my life. It isn't bluff, and it isn't a trance, either, like some of 'em have— it's plain nerve. You've certainly got to hand it to him.

(*He shakes his head in frank admiration.*)

Father Daly. (*Sorrowfully*) That's the pity of it—that a man with all his courage hasn't a better use for it.

Even now, it's very difficult for me to reconcile his character, as I see it, with what we know he's done.

The Warden. (*Continues to shake his head*) He's got my goat, all right.

Father Daly. (*With a slight grimace*) Yes, and he's got mine, too.

The Warden. When he sent for you tonight, I hoped he was going to talk.

Father Daly. He did talk, very freely.

The Warden. What about?

Father Daly. (*Smiles faintly, and sits beside the desk*) Most everything.

The Warden. (*Looks up quickly*) Himself?

Father Daly. No. That seems to be the only subject he isn't interested in.

The Warden. (*Sits up to his desk, and leans upon it with both elbows*) He still won't give you any hint about who he really is?

Father Daly. Not the slightest. He doesn't intend to, either. He intends to die as a man of mystery to us. Sometimes I wonder if he isn't just as much of a mystery to himself.

The Warden. Oh, he's trying to shield somebody, that's all. James Dyke isn't his right name—we know that; and we know all the rest of his story is a fake, too. Well, where's his motive? I'll tell you where it is. It's to keep his family and his friends, wherever they are, from knowing what's happened to him. Lots of 'em have the same idea but I never knew one to carry it as far as this, before. You've certainly got to hand it to him. All we know is that we've got a man under sentence; and we don't know who he is, or where he comes from, or anything else about him, any more than we did four months ago.

Father Daly. It takes moral courage for a man to shut himself away from his family and his friends like that. They would have comforted him.

The Warden. Not necessarily. What time is it?

Father Daly. Half-past eleven.

The Warden. (*Rises and walks over to peer out of one of the barred windows*) I guess I'm getting too old for this sort of thing. A necktie party didn't use to bother me so much; but every time one comes along nowadays, I've got the blue devils beforehand and afterward. And this one is just about the limit.

Father Daly. It certainly isn't a pleasant duty even with the worst of them.

The Warden. (*Wheels back abruptly*) But what gets *me* is why I should hate this one more than any of the others. The boy is guilty as hell.

Father Daly. Yes, he killed a man. "Wilfully, feloniously, and with malice aforethought."

The Warden. And he pleaded guilty. So he deserves just what he's going to get.

Father Daly. That is the law. But has it ever occurred to you, Warden, that every now and then when a criminal behaves in a rather gentlemanly fashion to us, we instinctively think of him as just a little less of a criminal?

The Warden. Yes, it has. But, all the same, this front of his makes me as nervous as the devil. He pleaded guilty all right, but he don't *act* guilty. I feel just as if tonight I was going to do something every bit as criminal as he did. I can't help it. And when I get to feeling like that, why, I guess it's pretty nearly time I sent in my resignation.

Father Daly. (*Reflectively*) His whole attitude has been very remarkable. Why, only a few minutes ago I found myself comparing it with the fortitude that the Christian martyrs carried to their death, and yet—

The Warden. He's no martyr.

Father Daly. I know it. And he's anything in the world but a Christian. That was just what I was going to say.

The Warden. Has he got any religious streak in him at all?

Father Daly. I'm afraid he hasn't. He listens to me very attentively, but— (*He shrugs his shoulders.*) It's only because I offer him companionship. Anybody else would do quite as well—and any other topic would suit him better.

The Warden. Well, if he wants to face God as a heathen, *we* can't force him to change his mind.

Father Daly. (*With gentle reproach*) No, but we can never give up trying to save his immortal soul. And his soul tonight seems as dark and foreboding to me as a haunted house would seem to the small boys down in Wethersfield. But I haven't given up hope.

The Warden. No—you wouldn't.

Father Daly. Are you going to talk with him again yourself?

The Warden. (*Opens a drawer of his desk, and brings out a large envelope*) I'll have to. I've still got some Liberty Bonds that belong to him. (*He gazes at the envelope, and smiles grimly.*) That was a funny thing— when the newspaper syndicate offered him twenty-five hundred for his autobiography, he jumped at it so quick I was sure he wanted the money for something or other. (*He slaps the envelope on the desk.*) But now the bonds are here, waiting for him, he won't say what to do with 'em. Know why? (Father Daly *shakes his head.*) Why, of course you do! Because the story he wrote was pure bunk from start to finish and the only reason he jumped at the chance of writing it was so's he could pull the wool over everybody's head a little farther. He don't want the bonds, but I've got to do *something* with 'em. (*He pushes a button on the desk.*) And besides, I want to make one more try at finding out who he is.

Father Daly. Shall I go with you to see him or do you want to see him alone?

The Warden. (*Sits deliberating with one hand at his forehead, and the other hand tapping the desk*) Father, you gave me a thought—I believe I'm going to do something tonight that's never been done before in this prison—that is to say—not in all the twenty-eight years that *I've* been warden.

Father Daly. What's that?

The Warden. (*Who has evidently come to an important decision, raps the desk more forcibly with his knuckles*) Instead of our going to see him, I'll have that boy brought into this office and let him sit here with you and me until the time comes for us all to walk through that door to the execution room.

Father Daly. (*Startled*) What on earth is your idea in doing a thing like that?

The Warden. Because maybe if he sits here awhile with just you and me, and we go at him right, he'll loosen up and tell us about himself. It'll be different from being in his cell; it'll be sort of free and easy, and maybe he'll weaken. And then, besides, if we take him to the scaffold through this passageway, maybe I can keep the others quiet. If they don't know when the job's being done, they may behave 'emselves. I don't want any such yelling and screeching tonight as we had with that

Greek. (*A* Jailer *in blue uniform enters from the deputy's room and stands waiting.*) Dan, I want you to get Dyke and bring him to me here. (*The* Jailer *stares blankly at him and the* Warden's *voice takes on an added note of authority.*) Get Dyke and bring him in here to me.

The Jailer. Yes, sir, (*He starts to obey the order but halts in the doorway and turns as the* Warden *speaks again. It is apparent that the* Warden *is a strict disciplinarian of the prison staff.*)

The Warden. Oh, Dan!

The Jailer. Yes, sir?

The Warden. How nearly ready are they?

The Jailer. They'll be all set in ten or fifteen minutes, sir. Twenty minutes at the outside.

The Warden. (*Very sharp and magisterial*) Now, I don't want any hitch or delay in this thing tonight. If there is, somebody's going to get in awful Dutch with me. Pass that along.

The Jailer. There won't be none, sir.

The Warden. When everything's ready—not a second before—you let me know.

The Jailer. Yes, sir.

The Warden. I'll be right here with Dyke and Father Daly.

The Jailer. (*Eyes widening*) Here?

The Warden. (*Peremptorily*) Yes, here!

The Jailer. (*Crushes down his astonishment*) Yes, sir.

The Warden. When everything and everybody is ready, you come from the execution room through the passage —(*He gestures towards the nearer door on the right.*) open that door quietly and stand there.

The Jailer. Yes, sir.

The Warden. You don't have to say anything, and I don't *want* you to say anything. Just stand there. That all clear?

The Jailer. Yes, sir.

The Warden. That'll be the signal for us to start—understand?

The Jailer. Yes, sir.

The Warden. (*Draws a deep breath*) All right. Now bring Dyke to me.

The Jailer. Yes, sir. (*He goes out dazedly.*)

Father Daly. What about the witnesses and the reporters?

The Warden. They're having their sandwiches and coffee now—the deputy'll have 'em seated in another ten or fifteen minutes. Let 'em wait. (*His voice becomes savage.*) I'd like to poison the lot of 'em. Reporters! Witnesses! (*The telephone bell rings.*) Hello—yes—yes— what's that?—Yes, yes, right here—who wants him? (*To* Father Daly) Father, it's the Governor! (*His expression is tense.*)

Father Daly. (*His voice also gives evidence of incredulity and hope.*) What! (*He walks swiftly over to the desk.*) Is it about Dyke?

The Warden. Ssh. (*He turns to the telephone.*) Yes, this is Warden Holt speaking. Hello—oh, hello, Governor Fuller, how are you? Oh, I'm between grass and hay, thanks. Well, this isn't my idea of a picnic exactly—yes—yes—Oh, I should say in about half an hour or so—everything's just about ready. (*His expression gradually relaxes, and* Father Daly, *with a little sigh and shake of the head, turns away.*) Oh, no, there won't be any slip-up—yes, we made the regular tests, one this afternoon and another at nine o'clock tonight—

Oh, no, Governor, nothing can go wrong—Well, according to the law I've got to get it done as soon as possible after midnight, but you're the Governor of the state—How long?—Certainly, Governor, I can hold it off as long as you want me to— What say?—A *girl!*— You're going to send her to me?—you *have* sent her!— she ought to be here by this time?—All right, Governor, I'll ring you up when it's over. Good-bye. (*He hangs up the receiver, mops his forehead with his handkerchief, and turns to* Father Daly *in great excitement.*) Did you get *that?* Some girl thinks Dyke's her long-lost brother, and she's persuaded the old man to let her come out here tonight—he wants me to hold up the job until she's had a chance to see him. She's due here any minute, he says —in his own car—escorted by his own private secretary! Can you beat it?

Father Daly. (*Downcast*) Poor girl!

The Warden. (*Blots his forehead vigorously*) For a minute there I thought it was going to be a reprieve at the very least. Whew!

Father Daly. So did I.

(*The door from the deputy's room is opened, and* Dyke *comes in, followed immediately by the* Jailer. Dyke *halts just inside the door and waits passively to be told what to do next. He has a lean, pale face, with a high forehead, good eyes, and a strong chin; his mouth is ruled in a firm straight line. His wavy hair is prematurely gray. His figure has the elasticity of youth, but he might pass among strangers either as a man of forty, or as a man of twenty-five, depending upon the mobility of his features at a given moment. He is dressed in a dark shirt open at the throat, dark trousers without belt or suspenders, and soft slippers. The* Jailer *receives a nod from the* Warden, *and goes out promptly, closing the door behind him.*)

The Warden. (*Swings half-way around in his swivel chair*) Sit down, Dyke. (*He points to the chair at the right of his desk.*)

Dyke. Thanks. (*He goes directly to the chair and sits down.*)

The Warden. (*Leans back, and surveys him thoughtfully; Father Daly remains in the background.*) Dyke, you've been here under my charge for nearly four months and I want to tell you that from first to last you've behaved yourself like a gentleman.

Dyke. (*His manner is vaguely cynical without being in the least impertinent.*) Why should I make you any trouble?

The Warden. Well, you *haven't* made me any trouble, and I've tried to show what I think about it. I've made you every bit as comfortable as the law would let me.

Dyke. You've been very kind to me. (*He glances over his shoulder at the chaplain.*) And you, too, Father.

The Warden. I've had you brought in here to stay from now on. (Dyke *looks inquiringly at him.*) No, you won't have to go back to your cell again. You're to stay right here with Father Daly and me.

Dyke. (*Carelessly*) All right.

The Warden. (*Piqued by this cool reception of the distinguished favor*) You don't seem to understand that I'm doing something a long way out of the ordinary for you.

Dyke. Oh, yes, I do, but maybe *you* don't understand why it doesn't give me much of a thrill.

Father Daly. (*Comes forward*) My son, the Warden is only trying to do you one more kindness.

Dyke. I know he is, Father, but the Warden isn't taking

very much of a gamble. From now on, one place is about the same as another.

The Warden. What do you mean?

Dyke. (*His voice is very faintly sarcastic.*) Why, I mean that I'm just as much a condemned prisoner here as when I was in my cell. That door (*He points to it.*) leads right *back* to my cell. Outside those windows are armed guards every few feet. You yourself can't get through the iron door in that anteroom (*He indicates the door to the left.*) until somebody on the outside unlocks it; and I know as well as you do where *that* door (*He points to the nearer door on the right.*) leads to.

The Warden. (*Stiffly*) Would you rather wait in your cell?

Dyke. Oh, no, this is a little pleasanter. Except—

The Warden. Except what?

Dyke. In my cell, I could smoke.

The Warden. (*Shrugs his shoulders*) What do you want —cigar or cigarette?

Dyke. A cigarette, if it's all the same.

(*The* Warden *opens a drawer of his desk, takes out a box of cigarettes, removes one and hands it to* Dyke. *The* Warden *striking a match, lights* Dyke's *cigarette, and then carefully puts out the match.*)

Dyke. (*Smiles faintly*) Thanks. You're a good host.

The Warden. Dyke, before it's too late I wish you'd think over what Father Daly and I've said to you so many times.

Dyke. I've thought of nothing else.

The Warden. Then—as man to man—and this is your last chance—who are you?

Dyke. (*Inspects his cigarette*) Who am I? James Dyke—a murderer.

The Warden. That isn't your real name and we know it.

Dyke. You're not going to execute a name—you'er going to execute a *man*. What difference does it make whether you call me Dyke or something else?

The Warden. You had another name once. What was it?

Dyke. If I had, I've forgotten it.

Father Daly. Your mind is made up, my son?

Dyke. Yes, Father, it is.

The Warden. Dyke.

Dyke. Yes, sir?

The Warden. Do you see this pile of letters? (*He places his hand over it.*)

Dyke. Yes, sir.

The Warden. (*Fingers them*) Every one of these letters is about the same thing and all put together we've got maybe four thousand of 'em. These here are just a few samples.

Dyke. What about them?

The Warden. We've had letters from every State in the Union and every province in Canada. We've had fifteen or twenty from England, four or five from France, two from Australia and one from Russia.

Dyke. Well?

The Warden. (*Inclines towards him*) Do you know what every one of those letters says—what four thousand different people are writing to me about?

Dyke. No, sir.

The Warden. (*Speaks slowly and impressively*) Who *are* you—and are you the missing son—or brother—or husband—or sweetheart?

Dyke. (*Flicks his cigarette ashes to the floor*) Have you answered them?

The Warden. No, I couldn't. I want you to:

Dyke. How's that?

The Warden. I want you to tell me who you are. (Dyke *shakes his head.*) Can't you see you *ought* to do it?

Dyke. No, sir, I can't exactly see that. Suppose you explain it to me.

The Warden. (*Suddenly*) You're trying to shield somebody, aren't you?

Dyke. Yes—no, I'm not!

The Warden. (*Glances at* Father Daly *and nods with elation*) Who is it? Your family?

Dyke. I said I'm not.

The Warden. But first, you said you were.

Dyke. That was a slip of the tongue.

The Warden. (*Has grown persuasive*) Dyke, just listen to me a minute. Don't be narrow, look at this thing in a big, broad way. Suppose you should tell me your real name, and I publish it, it'll bring an awful lot of sorrow, let's say, to *one* family, *one* home, and that's your own. That's probably what you're thinking about. Am I right? You want to spare your family and I don't blame you. On the surface, it sure would look like a mighty white thing for you to do. But look at it *this* way: suppose you came out with the truth, flat-footed, why, you might put all that sorrow into *one* home—your own— but at the same time you'd be putting an immense amount of relief in four thousand—others. Don't you get that? Don't you figure you owe something to all these other people?

Dyke. Not a thing.

Father Daly. (*Has been fidgeting*) My boy, the Warden is absolutely right. You do owe something to the other people—you owe them peace of mind—and for the sake of all those thousands of poor, distressed women, who imagine God knows what, I beg of you to tell us who you are.

Dyke. Father, I simply can't do it.

Father Daly. Think carefully, my boy, think very carefully. We're not asking out of idle curiosity.

Dyke. I know that, but please don't let's talk about it any more. (*To the* Warden) You can answer those letters whenever you want to, and you can say I'm not the man they're looking for. That'll be the truth, too. Because I haven't any mother—or father—or sister—or wife—or sweetheart. That's fair enough, isn't it?

Father Daly. (*Sighs wearily*) As you will, my son.

The Warden. Dyke, there's one more thing.

Dyke. Yes?

The Warden. Here are the Liberty Bonds (*He takes up the large envelope from his desk.*) that belong to you. Twenty-five hundred dollars in real money.

Dyke. (*Removes the bonds and examines them*) Good-looking, aren't they?

The Warden. (*Casually*) What do you want me to do with them?

Dyke. Well, I can't very well take them with me, so, under the circumstances, I'd like to put them where they'll do the most good.

The Warden. (*More casually yet*) Who do you want me to send 'em to?

Dyke. (*Laughs quietly*) Now, Warden Holt, you didn't think you were going to catch me that way, did you?

The Warden. (*Scowls*) Who'll I send 'em to? I can't keep 'em here, and I can't destroy 'em. What do you want to do with 'em?

Dyke. (*Ponders diligently and tosses the envelopes to the desk*) I don't know. I'll think of something to do with them. I'll tell you in just a minute. Is there anything else?

The Warden. Not unless you want to make some sort of statement.

Dyke. No, I guess I've said everything. I killed a man and I'm not sorry for it—that is, I'm not sorry I killed that particular person. I—

Father Daly. (*Raises his hand*) Repentance—

Dyke. (*Raises his own hand in turn*) I've heard that repentance, Father, is the sick bed of the soul—and mine is very well and flourishing. The man deserved to be killed; he wasn't fit to live. It was my duty to kill him, and I did it. I'd never struck a man in anger in all my life, but when I knew what that fellow had done, I knew I had to kill him, and I did it deliberately and intentionally—and carefully. I knew what I was doing, and I haven't any excuse—that is, I haven't any excuse that satisfies the law. Now, I learned pretty early in life that whatever you do in this world you have to pay for in one way or another. If you kill a man, the price you have to pay is this (*He makes a gesture which sweeps the entire room.*) and that (*He points to the nearer door on the right.*) and I'm going to pay it. That's all there is to that. And an hour from now, while my body is lying in there, if a couple of angel policemen grab my soul and haul it up before God—

Father Daly. (*Profoundly shocked*) My boy, my boy, please—

Dyke. I beg your pardon, Father. I don't mean to trample on anything that's sacred to you, but what I do mean to say is this: If I've got to be judged by God Almighty for the crime of murder, I'm not afraid, because the other fellow will certainly be there, too, won't he? And when God hears the whole story and both sides of it, which *you* never heard and never will— and they never heard it in the court room, either—why, then, if he's any kind of a God at all, I'm willing to take my chances with the other fellow. That's how concerned I am about the hereafter. And, if it'll make you feel any better, Father, why I *do* rather think there's going to be a hereafter. I read a book once that said a milligram of musk will give out perfume for seven thousand years, and a milligram of radium will give out light for *seventy* thousand. Why shouldn't a soul—mine, for instance— live more than twenty-seven? But if there *isn't* any hereafter—if we just die and are dead and that's all—why, I'm still not sorry and I'm not afraid, because I'm quits with the other fellow—the law is quits with me, and it's all balanced on the books. And that's all there is to that.

(*An attendant enters from the anteroom.*)

The Warden. Well? What is it?

The Attendant. Visitor to see you, sir. With note from Governor Fuller. (*He presents it.*)

The Warden. (*Barely glances at the envelope*) Oh! A young woman?

The Attendant. Yes, sir.

The Warden. Is Mrs. Case there?

The Attendant. Yes, sir.

The Warden. Have the girl searched, and then take her into the anteroom and wait till I call you.

The Attendant. Yes, sir. (*He goes out.*)

The Warden. Dyke, a young woman has just come to see you—do you want to see her?

Dyke. I don't think so. What does she want?

The Warden. She thinks maybe she's your sister, and she's come a thousand miles to find out.

Dyke. She's wrong. I haven't any sister.

The Warden. (*Hesitates*) Will I tell her that, or do you want to tell it to her yourself?

Dyke. Oh, you tell her.

The Warden. All right. (*He starts to rise but resumes his seat as* Dyke *speaks.*)

Dyke. Just a second—she's come a thousand miles to see me, did you say?

The Warden. Yes, and she's got special permission from the Governor to talk to you—that is, with my O.K.

Dyke. A year ago, nobody'd have crossed the street to look at me, and now they come a thousand miles!

Father Daly. This is one of your debts to humanity, my boy. It wouldn't take you two minutes to see her, and, if you don't, after she's made that long journey in hope and dread and suffering—

Dyke. Where can I talk with her—here?

The Warden. Yes.

Dyke. Alone? (*The* Warden *is doubtful.*) Why, you don't need to be afraid. I haven't the faintest idea who the girl is, but if she happens to be some poor misguided sentimental fool, with a gun or a pocket full of cyanide of potassium, she's wasting her time. I wouldn't cheat the

sovereign state of Connecticut for anything in the
world—not even to please a young lady.

The Warden. Dyke, there's something about **you**
that gets everybody.

Dyke. How about the jury?

The Warden. You've got a sort of way with you—

Dyke. How about that spread-eagle district attorney?

The Warden. I'm going to let you talk with that girl in
here—alone.

Dyke. Thanks.

The Warden. It's a sort of thing that's never been done
before, but if I put you on your honor—

Dyke. (*Cynically*) My honor! Thank you, so much.

Father Daly. Warden, are you sure it's wise?

Dyke. Father, I'm disappointed in you. Do you imagine
I'd do anything that could reflect on Warden Holt—
or you—or the young lady—or *me?*

The Warden. Father, will you take Dyke into the
deputy's room? I want to speak to the young lady first.

Father Daly. Certainly. Come, my boy. (Father Daly
and Dyke *start towards the deputy's room.*)

The Warden. I'll call you in just a couple of minutes.

Dyke. We promise not to run away. (*They go out
together.*)

The Warden. (*Calls*) Wilson! (*The* Attendant *enters
from the left.*)

The Attendant. Yes, sir.

The Warden. Is the girl there?

The Attendant. Yes, sir.

The Warden. Frisked?

The Attendant. Yes, sir.

The Warden.   Everything all right?

The Attendant.   Yes, sir.

The Warden.   (*Throws away his cigar*)   Bring her in.

The Attendant.   Yes, sir. (*He speaks through the door at the left.*)   Step this way, Miss. This here's the Warden.

(*A young girl appears on the threshold, and casts about in mingled curiosity and apprehension. She is fresh and wholesome, and rather pretty; but her manner betrays a certain spiritual aloofness from the ultra-modern world—a certain delicate reticence of the flesh—which immediately separates her from the metropolitan class. Indeed, she is dressed far too simply for a metropolitan girl of her age; she wears a blue tailored suit with deep white cuffs and a starched white sailor-collar, and a small blue hat which fits snugly over her fluffy hair. Her costume is not quite conservative enough to be literally old-fashioned, but it hints at the taste and repression of an old-fashioned home. She is neither timid nor aggressive; she is self-unconscious. She looks at the Warden squarely, but not in boldness, and yet not in feminine appeal; she has rather the fearlessness of a girl who has lost none of her illusions about men in general. Her expression is essentially serious; it conveys, however, the idea that her seriousness is due to her present mission, and that ordinarily she takes an active joy in the mere pleasure of existence.*)

The Warden.   (*He had expected a very different type of visitor, so that he is somewhat taken aback.*)   All right, Wilson.

The Attendant.   Yes, sir. (*He goes out.*)

The Warden.   (*With grave deference, half rises*)   Will you sit down?

The Girl.   Why—thank you very much. (*She sits in the chair beside the desk and regards him trustfully.*)

The Warden. (*He is palpably affected by her youth and innocence, and he is not quite sure how best to proceed, but eventually he makes an awkward beginning.*) You've had an interview with the Governor, I understand?

The Girl. Yes, sir. I was with him almost an hour.

The Warden. And you want to see Dyke, do you?

The Girl. Yes, sir. I *hope* I'm not—too late.

The Warden. No, you're not too late. (*He is appraising her carefully.*) But I want to ask you a few questions beforehand. (*Her reaction of uncertainty induces him to soften his tone.*) There isn't anything to get upset about. I just want to make it easier for you, not harder. Where do you live?

The Girl. In Ohio.

The Warden. (*Very kindly*) What place?

The Girl. In Pennington, sir. It's a little town not far from Columbus.

The Warden. And you live out there with your father and mother?

The Girl. No, sir—just my mother and I. My father died when I was a little baby.

The Warden. Why didn't your mother come here herself, instead of sending you?

The Girl. She couldn't. She's sick.

The Warden. I see. Have you any brothers or sisters?

The Girl. (*Slightly more at ease*) Just one brother, sir— this one. He and I were the only children. We were very fond of each other.

The Warden. He was considerably older than you?

The Girl. Oh, yes. He's ten years older.

The Warden. Why did he leave home?

The Girl. I don't really know, sir, except he just wanted to be in the city. Pennington's pretty small.

The Warden. How long is it since you've seen him?

The Girl. It's eight years.

The Warden. (*His voice is almost paternal.*) As long as that? Hm! And how old are you now?

The Girl. I'm almost eighteen.

The Warden. (*Repeats slowly*) Almost eighteen. Hm! And are you sure after all this time you'd recognize your brother if you saw him?

The Girl. Well—(*She looks down, as if embarrassed to make the admission.*)—of course I *think* so, but maybe I couldn't. You see, I was only a little girl when he went away—he wasn't a bad boy, sir, I don't think he could ever be really bad—but if this *is* my brother, why he's been in a great deal of trouble and you know that trouble makes people look different.

The Warden. Yes, it does. But what makes you think this man Dyke may be your brother—and why didn't you think of it sooner? The case has been in the papers for the last six months.

The Girl. Why, it wasn't until last Tuesday that mother saw a piece in the *Journal*—that's the Columbus paper—that he'd written all about himself, and there was one little part of it that sounded so like Joe—like the funny way he used to say things—and then there was a picture that looked the least little *bit* like him—well, mother just wanted me to come East and find out for sure.

The Warden. It's too bad she couldn't come herself. She'd probably know him whether he'd changed or not.

The Girl. Yes, sir. But I'll do the best I can.

The Warden. When was the last time you heard from him, and where was he, and what was he doing?

The Girl. Why, it's about five or six years since we had a letter from Joe. He was in Seattle, Washington.

The Warden. What doing?

The Girl. I don't remember. At home, though, he worked in the stationery store. He liked books.

The Warden. (*Suspiciously*) Why do you suppose he didn't write home?

The Girl. I—couldn't say. He was just—thoughtless.

The Warden. Wasn't in trouble of any kind?

The Girl. Oh, *no*! Never. That is—unless he's—here now.

The Warden. (*Deliberates*) How are you going to tell him?

The Girl. I don't know what you mean.

The Warden. Why, you say maybe you wouldn't know him even if you saw him—and I'll guarantee this man Dyke won't help you out very much. How do you think you're going to tell? Suppose he don't want to be recognized by you or anybody else? Suppose he's so ashamed of himself he—

The Girl. I'd thought of that. I'm just going to talk to him—ask him questions—about things he and I used to do together—I'll watch his face, and if he's my brother, I'm sure I can tell.

The Warden. (*With tolerant doubt*) What did you and your brother ever use to do that would help you out now?

The Girl. He used to play games with me when I was a little girl, and tell me stories—that's what I'm counting on mostly—the stories.

The Warden. I'm afraid—

The Girl. Especially Shakespeare stories.

The Warden. Shakespeare!

The Girl. Why, yes. He used to get the plots of the plays—all the Shakespeare plays—out of a book by a man named Lamb, and then he'd tell me the stories in his own words. It was wonderful!

The Warden. I'm certainly afraid he—

The Girl. But best of all he'd learn some of the speeches from the plays themselves. He liked to do it—he was sure he was going to be an actor or something—he was in all the high school plays, always. And then he'd teach some of the speeches to me, and we'd say them to each other. And one thing—every night he'd sit side of my bed, and when I got sleepy there were two speeches we'd always say to each other, like good-night—two speeches out of *Romeo and Juliet*, and then I'd go to sleep. I can see it all. (*The* Warden *shakes his head.*) Why do you do that?

The Warden. This boy isn't your brother.

The Girl. Do you think he isn't?

The Warden. I *know* he isn't.

The Girl. How do you?

The Warden. This boy never heard of Shakespeare— much less learned him. (*He presses a button on his desk.*) Oh, I'll let you see him for yourself, only you might as well be prepared. (*The* Attendant *enters from the ante-room.*) Tell Dyke and Father Daly to come in here— they're in the deputy's room.

The Attendant. Yes, sir. (*He crosses behind the* Warden, *and goes off to the right.*)

The Warden. If he turns out to be your brother— which he won't—you can have, say, an hour with him. If he don't, you'll oblige me by cutting it as short as you can.

The Girl. You see, I've got to tell mother something perfectly definite. She's worried so long about him, and —and *now* the suspense is perfectly terrible for her.

The Warden. I can understand that. You're a plucky girl.

The Girl. Of course, it would be awful for us if this *is* Joe, but even that would be better for mother than just to stay awake nights, and wonder and wonder, and never *know* what became of him. (*The* Attendant *opens the door of the Deputy's room, and when* Dyke *and* Father Daly *have come in, he crosses again behind the* Warden, *and is going out at the left when the* Warden *signs to him and he stops.*)

The Warden. (*Gets to his feet*) Dyke, this is the young lady that's come all the way from Pennington, Ohio, to see you.

Dyke. (*Who has been talking in an undertone to* Father Daly, *raises his head quickly*) Yes, sir?

The Warden. I've decided you can talk with her here— alone. (*The* Girl *has risen, breathless, and stands fixed;* Dyke *inspects her coldly from head to foot.*)

Dyke. Thank you. It won't take long.

The Warden. (*Has been scanning the girl's expression; now, as he sees that she has neither recognized* Dyke *nor failed to recognize him, he makes a little grimace in confirmation of his own judgment.*) Father Daly and I'll stay in the deputy's office. We'll leave the door open. Wilson, you stand in the anteroom with the door open.

Dyke. (*Bitterly*) My honor!

The Warden. What say?

Dyke. I didn't say anything.

The Warden. (*To the* Girl) Will you please remember what I told you about the time?

The Girl. Oh, yes, sir.

The Warden. Come, Father. (*They go off into the Deputy's room, and the* Attendant, *at a nod from the* Warden, *goes off at the left.*)

(Dyke *and the* Girl *are now facing each other;* Dyke *is well-poised and insouciant and gives the impression of complete indifference to the moment. The* Girl, *on the other hand, is deeply agitated and her agitation is gradually increased by* Dyke's *own attitude.*)

The Girl. (*After several efforts to speak*) Mother sent me to see you.

Dyke. (*Politely callous*) Yes?

The Girl. (*Compelled to drop her eyes*) You see, we haven't seen or heard of my brother Joe for ever so long, and mother thought—after what we read in the papers—

Dyke. That I might be your brother Joe?

The Girl. (*Obviously relieved*) Yes, that's it.

Dyke. Well, you can easily see that I'm not your brother, can't you?

The Girl. (*Stares at him again*) I'm not sure. You look a little like him, just as the picture in the paper did, but then again, it's so long— (*She shakes her head dubiously.*) and I'd thought of Joe so differently—

Dyke. (*His manner is somewhat indulgent, as though to a child.*) As a matter of fact, I couldn't be *your* brother, or anybody else's brother, because I never had a sister. So that rather settles it.

The Girl. Honestly?

Dyke. Honestly.

The Girl. (*Unconvinced, becomes more appealing*) What's your real name?

Dyke. Dyke—James Dyke.

The Girl. That's sure enough your name?

Dyke. Sure enough. You don't think I'd tell a lie at this stage of the game, do you?

The Girl. (*Musing*) No, I don't believe you would. Where do you come from—I mean where were you born?

Dyke. In Canada, but I've lived all over.

The Girl. Didn't you ever live in Ohio?

Dyke. No. Never.

The Girl. What kind of work did you do—what was your business?

Dyke. Oh, I'm sort of Jack-of-all-trades. I've been everything a man *could* be—except a success.

The Girl. Do you like books?

Dyke. Books?

The Girl. Yes—books to read.

Dyke. I don't read when there's anything better to do. I've read a lot here.

The Girl. Did you ever sell books—for a living, I mean?

Dyke. Oh, no.

The Girl. (*Growing confused*) I hope you don't mind my asking so many questions. But I—

Dyke. No—go ahead, if it'll relieve your mind any.

The Girl. You went to school somewhere, of course,—high school?

Dyke. No, I never got that far.

The Girl. Did you ever want to be an actor? Or *were* you ever?

Dyke. No, just a convict.

The Girl. (*Helplessly*) Do you know any poetry?

Dyke.   Not to speak of.

The Girl.   (*Delays a moment, and then, watching him very earnestly, she recites just above her breath*)

"Thou knowst the mask of night is on my face
Else would a maiden blush bepaint my cheek
For that which . . ."

(*Realizing that* Dyke's *expression is one of utter vacuity she falters, and breaks off the quotation, but she continues to watch him unwaveringly.*)   Don't you know what that is?

Dyke.   No, but to tell the truth, it sounds sort of silly to *me*. Doesn't it to you?

The Girl.   (*Her intonation has become slightly forlorn, but she gathers courage, and puts him to one more test.*)

"Good-night, good-night, parting is such sweet sorrow
That I shall say good-night till it be morrow."

Dyke.   (*His mouth twitches in amusement.*)   Eh?

The Girl.   What comes next?

Dyke.   Good Lord, I don't know.

The Girl.   (*Gazes intently, almost imploringly, at him as though she is making a struggle to read his mind; then she relaxes and holds out her hand.*)   Good-bye. You—you're *not* Joe, are you?   I—had to come and find out, though. I hope I've not made you too unhappy.

Dyke.   (*Ignores her hand*)   You're not going now?

The Girl.   (*Spiritless*)   Yes. I promised the—is he the Warden? that man in there?—I said I'd go right away if you weren't my brother. And you aren't, so—

Dyke.   You're going back to your mother?

The Girl.   Yes.

Dyke.   I'm surprised that she sent a girl like you on a sorry errand like this, instead of—

The Girl.   She's very sick.

Dyke.   Oh, that's too bad.

The Girl.   (*Twisting her handkerchief*)   No, she's not well at all. And most of it's from worrying about Joe.

Dyke.   Still, when you tell her that her son isn't a murderer—at least, that he isn't *this* one—that'll comfort her a good deal, won't it?

The Girl.   (*Reluctantly*)   Yes, I think maybe it will, only—

Dyke.   Only what?

The Girl.   I don't think mother'll ever be *really* well again until she finds out for certain where Joe is and what's become of him.

Dyke.   (*Shakes his head compassionately*)   Mothers ought not to be treated like that. I wish I'd treated *mine* better. By the way, you didn't tell me what your name is.

The Girl.   Josephine Paris.

Dyke.   (*Is suddenly attentive*)   Paris? That's an unusual name. I've heard it somewhere, too.

The Girl.   Just like the name of the city—in France.

Dyke.   (*Knitting his brows*)   And your brother's name was Joseph?

The Girl.   Yes—they used to call us Joe and Josie— that's funny, isn't it?

Dyke.   (*Thoughtfully*)   No, I don't think it's so very funny. I rather like it. (*He passes his hand over his forehead as if trying to coerce his memory.*)

The Girl.   What's the matter?

Dyke.   (*Frowning*)   I was thinking of something—now, what on earth was that boy's name! Wait a minute, don't tell me—wait a minute—I've got it! (*He punc-*

tuates his triumph with one fist in the palm of the other hand.)
Joseph Anthony Paris!

The Girl. (*Amazed*) Why, that's his name! That's Joe! How did you ever—

Dyke. (*His manner is very forcible and convincing.*) Wait! Now listen carefully to what I say, and don't interrupt me, because we've only got a minute, and I want you to get this all straight, so you can tell your mother. When the war came along I enlisted and I was overseas for four years—with the Canadians. Early one morning we'd staged a big trench raid, and there was an officer who'd been wounded coming back, and was lying out there in a shell-hole under fire. The Jerries were getting ready for a raid of their own, so they were putting down a box barrage with light guns and howitzers and a few heavies. This officer was lying right in the middle of it. Well, all of a sudden a young fellow dashed out of a trench not far from where I was, and went for that officer. He had to go through a curtain of shells and, more than that, they opened on him with rifles and machine guns. The chances were just about a million to one against him, and he must have known it, but he went out just the same. He got the officer in his arms and started back, but he'd only gone a few yards when a five point nine landed right on top of the two of them. Afterward, we got what was left—the identification tag was still there—and that was the name— Joseph Anthony Paris!

The Girl. (*Carries both hands to her breast*) Oh!

Dyke. If that was your brother's name, then you can tell your mother that he died like a brave man and a soldier, three years ago, in France.

The Girl. Joe—my brother Joe—is dead?

Dyke. On the field of battle. It was one of the wonderful, heroic things that went almost unnoticed, as so many of them did. If an officer had seen it, there'd have been a decoration for your mother to keep and remember him by.

The Girl. And you were there—and saw it?

Dyke. I was there and saw it. It was three years ago. That's why you and your mother haven't heard from him. And if you don't believe what I've said, why, you just write up to Ottawa and get the official record. Of course (*He shrugs his shoulders contemptuously.*) those records are in terribly poor shape, but at least they can tell you what battalion he fought with, when he went overseas. Only you mustn't be surprised no matter whether they say he was killed in action, or died of wounds, or is missing, or even went through the whole war with his outfit, and was honorably discharged. They really don't know what happened to half the men. But I've told you the truth. And it certainly ought to make your mother happy when she knows that her boy died as a soldier, and not as a criminal.

The Girl. (*Is transfigured*) Yes, yes, it will!

Dyke. And does it make you happy, too?

The Girl. (*Nods repeatedly*) Yes. So happy—after what we were both afraid of—I can't even cry—yet. (*She brushes her eyes with her handkerchief.*) I can hardly wait to take it to her.

Dyke. (*Struck by a sudden inspiration*) I want to give you something else to take to her. (*He picks up from the desk the envelope containing the Liberty Bonds and seals it.*) I want you to give this to your mother from me. Tell her it's from a man who was at Vimy Ridge and saw your brother die, so it's a sort of memorial for him.

(*He touches her arm as she absently begins to tear open the envelope.*) No, don't you open it—let *her* do it.

The Girl. What is it? Can't I know?

Dyke. Never mind now, but give it to her. It's all I've got in the world and it's too late now for me to do anything else with it. And have your mother buy a little gold star to wear for her son—and you get one, too, and wear it—here— (*He touches his heart.*) Will you?

The Girl. Yes—I will. And yet somehow I'll almost feel that I'm wearing it for you, too.

Dyke. (*Shakes his head soberly*) Oh, no! You mustn't ever do that. I'm not fit to be mentioned in the same breath with a boy like your brother, and now I'm afraid it *is* time for you to go. I'm sorry, but—you'd better. I'm glad you came before it was too late, though.

The Girl. (*Gives him her hand*) Good-bye, and thank you. You've done more for me—and mother— than I could possibly tell you. And—and I'm so sorry for you—so *truly sorry*—I wish I could only do something to make you a tiny bit happier, too. Is there anything I could do?

Dyke. (*Stares at her and by degrees he becomes wistful*) Why—yes, there is. Only I— (*He leaves the sentence uncompleted.*)

The Girl. What is it?

Dyke. (*Looks away*) I can't tell you. I never should have let myself think of it.

The Girl. Please tell me. I want you to. For—for Joe's sake, tell what I can do.

Dyke. (*His voice is low and desolate.*) Well—in all the months I've been in this hideous place, you're the first girl I've seen. I didn't ever expect to see one again. I'd forgotten how much like angels women look. I've been

terribly lonesome tonight, especially, and if you really do
want to do something for me—for your brother's sake—
you see, you're going to leave me in just a minute and—
and I haven't any sister of my own, or anybody else, to
say good-bye to me—so, if you could—*really* say good-
bye— (*She gazes at him for a moment, understands, flushes,
and then slowly moves into his outstretched arms. He holds
her close to him, touches his lips to her forehead twice, and
releases her.*)

Dyke. (*Thickly*) Good-bye, my dear.

The Girl. Good-night. (*She endeavors to smile, but her
voice catches in her throat.*) Good-bye.

Dyke. (*Impulsively*) What is it?

The Girl. (*Shakes her head*) N-nothing.

Dyke. Nothing?

The Girl. (*Clutches her handkerchief tight in her palm*)
I was thinking—I was thinking what I used to say to my
brother—for good-night. (*She very nearly breaks down.*)
If I *only* could have—have said it to him just once more
—for good-bye.

Dyke. What was it?

The Girl. I—I told it to you once, and you said it was
silly.

Dyke. (*Softly*) Say it again.

The Girl. (*She cannot quite control her voice.*)

"Good-night, good-night, parting is such sweet sorrow
   That I shall say good-night till it be morrow."

(*She goes uncertainly towards the anteroom, hesitates,
almost turns back, and then with a choking sob she hurries
through the door and closes it behind her. For several
seconds* Dyke *stands rigidly intent upon that door; until
at length, without changing his attitude or his expression,
he speaks very tenderly and reminiscently.*)

"Sleep dwell upon thine eyes, peace in thy breast;
    Would *I* were sleep and peace, so sweet to rest."

(*The* Warden *and* Father Daly *come in quietly from the Deputy's room; and as they behold* Dyke, *how rapt and unconscious of them he is, they look at each other, questioningly. The* Warden *glances at the clock and makes as though to interrupt* Dyke's *solitary reflections but* Father Daly *quietly restrains him.*

The Chaplain *sits down in one of the chairs at the back wall; the* Warden *crosses on tiptoe and sits at his desk; he is excessively nervous and he continually refers to the clock.* Dyke *turns, as though unwillingly, from the door; there are depths in his eyes, and his thoughts are evidently far away. He sits in the chair to the right of the* Warden's *desk and leans outward, his right hand on his knee. He puts his left hand to his throat as though to protect it from a sudden pain. He gazes straight ahead into the unknown and speaks in reverie.*)

"Of all the wonders that I yet have heard,
    It seems to me most strange that men should fear;
Seeing that death, a necessary end,
    Will come when it will come."

(*He stops and muses for a time, while the* Warden *glances perplexedly at* Father Daly *to discover if the priest can interpret what* Dyke *is saying.* Father Daly *shakes his head. Abruptly* Dyke's *face is illumined by a new and welcome recollection; and again he speaks, while the* Warden *tries in vain to comprehend him.*)

"Cowards die many times before their death;
    The valiant never taste of death but once."

(*He stops again and shudders a trifle; his head droops and he repeats, barely above a whisper.*)

"The valiant never taste of death but once."

(The nearer door on the right is opened noiselessly and the Jailer, in obedience to his instructions, steps just inside the room and stands there mute. Father Daly and the Warden glance at the Jailer, and with significance at each other, and both rise, tardily. The Warden's hand, as it rests on his desk is seen to tremble. There is a moment of dead silence; presently Dyke lifts his head and catches sight of the motionless Attendant at the open door. With a quick intake of his breath, he starts half out of his seat and stares, fascinated; he sinks back slowly, and turns his head to gaze first at Father Daly and then at the Warden. The Warden averts his eyes, but Father Daly's expression is of supreme pity and encouragement. Involuntarily, Dyke's hand again goes creeping upward towards his throat, but he arrests it. He grasps the arms of his chair and braces himself; he rises then, and stands very erect, in almost the position of a soldier at attention.)

The Warden. *(Swallows hard)* Dyke!

Father Daly. *(Brushes past the Warden, his right hand lifted as though in benediction)* My son!

Dyke. *(Regards them fixedly; his voice is low and steady.)* All right, let's go.

(He faces about, and with his head held proud and high, and his shoulders squared to the world, he moves slowly towards the open door. Father Daly, with the light of his calling in his eyes, steps in line just ahead of Dyke. The Warden, his mouth set hard, falls behind. When they have all gone forward a pace or two, Father Daly begins to speak, and Dyke to reply, Father Daly's voice is strong and sweet; and Dyke speaks just after him, not mechanically, but in brave and unfaltering response.)

Father Daly. "I will lift up mine eyes unto the hills—"

Dyke. "The valiant never taste of death but once."

Father Daly. "From whence cometh my help."

Dyke. "The valiant never taste of death but once."

Father Daly. (*Has almost reached the door; his voice rises a semi-tone, and gains in emotion.*) "My help cometh from the Lord which made Heaven and earth."

Dyke. "The valiant never taste of death—but once."

When the Warden, *whose hands are tightly clenched, has passed the threshold, the* Jailer *follows and closes the door behind him. There is a very brief pause and then*

CURTAIN

Moon-Up

by ROBERT ARTHUR

CHARACTERS

Ma Holloway
Tom Holloway
Harry Holloway
Sheriff Dexter

TIME: *Half-past eight on an evening in September.*

PLACE: *The Holloway farmhouse, in an isolated section of the Kentucky hills.*

MOON-UP

Ma Holloway *is a mountain woman, old and feeble, confined to a wheel chair. But though physically weak, her will and spirit are strong. She wears a nondescript blue dress, with a shawl over her shoulders, and is working on a patchwork quilt which covers her knees and legs. Her grey hair is long and done in a tight knot at the nape of her neck. When she returns toward the end of the play, she wears an old-fashioned high-necked nightgown covered by a dark, old dressing gown; a blanket over her knees.*

Tom Holloway *is somewhere between thirty and forty. He is a big man, slow spoken, slow moving, gentle, but very masculine. He wears a faded blue shirt, work trousers and work shoes.*

Harry Holloway *is in his late twenties or early thirties. He is slighter than Tom; moves with nervous swiftness; speaks like a city man rather than a country man. Glib and quick of tongue, there is a deadly viciousness beneath his superficial good looks. He wears a nondescript suit of work clothes beneath a good topcoat, and wears also old shoes and a hat salvaged from someone's barn.*

Sheriff Dexter *is a short, burly man, blunter and harsher than Tom. He wears heavy shoes, an old suit, a well-worn mackinaw or heavy jacket, and a battered hat. He is forthright and aggressive in both speech and movement.*

The scene is the "sitting room" of the Holloway home in a sparsely populated district along the high banks of the Big Pebbly, a tumultuous tributary of the South Fork of the Ken-

tucky River. Crowded between the mountains and the river, the Holloway farm is stony and barren. It takes untiring effort to wring a living from it. The room itself reflects the poverty of the environment, but it reflects too the characters of Tom Holloway and his mother. It is simply, even primitively furnished, but it is neat. Everything is clean and in place.

On the right is a practical window, which must open and shut. It is, in fact, open a foot now, held in place by a small stick, as is necessary with windows that have no sashcords and weights. It is curtained in a cheap, faded but clean material, and has a battered shade pulled halfway down. At the right, rear, is a doorway that leads into the kitchen and sleeping quarters of the house. The door is partly open. In the rear, center, is a rough stone fireplace with a projecting wooden mantel. At the extreme left, rear, is a curtained alcove which serves as a storage space. Down left is the door which leads to the exterior. Below it is a small chest of drawers and on the wall near the chest is a telephone, preferably old-fashioned, placed unusually low so that Ma can reach it without getting out of her wheel chair.

Over the fireplace hangs an old rifle—not an antique, however. On the wall between the fireplace and the interior door up right is a large gaudy calendar, a Currier and Ives print, making a brave effort to brighten the room. On the fireplace mantel is a pipe and a small can of tobacco.

In the center of the room is a fair-sized table, a battered antique cherished by Ma because it was her mother's. On it are two lighted kerosene lamps, an old battery radio and a few papers and farm journals, neatly arranged. At the right of the table is an old wheel chair, and at the left a well-worn armchair. A small potted plant or two and one or two chromos, representing Ma Holloway's effort to bring color and warmth into the room, together with whatever else is necessary to satisfy the eye, complete the picture.

As the Curtain rises, Ma Holloway *is seated in the wheel chair, a shawl over her shoulders, a bright-colored patchwork quilt on which she is working, spread over her knees. She is old and feeble, but her face has an expression of serenity—the serenity that comes to women who have fought an environment so long that they know they can never win the fight, but will never admit to losing it.*

Tom, Ma's *older son, who is somewhere between thirty and forty, is sitting in the chair at the other end of the table, studying a mail-order catalogue. He wears faded but clean blue jeans and a work shirt. He is a big, slow-moving, gentle man—a marked contrast to the usual type that the mountains breed, hot-tempered, quick to blaze up, to shed blood, to cherish a grudge. As he moves around the room, he almost instinctively puts things to rights.*

It is half-past eight in the evening, and the only light comes from the two kerosene lamps and the feeble glow of the fire.

Author's Note: *To increase the readability, the regional dialect has been suggested here rather than literally transcribed. Everyday mountain speech would use "git" for "get," "hit" for "it," "hain't" for "ain't" (but would say "hain't it," not "hain't hit"), "yit" for "yet," "cain't" for "can't," etc. For production purposes, these usages would enhance the effect of the mountain locale; but equally with a few changes in wording the play could be laid anywhere in America—for that matter, almost anywhere in the world. For this is a story that could happen anywhere.*

Tom. (*He marks his place and puts down the catalogue, then crosses to the window.*) Reckon I better shut th' window, Ma. Gettin' chilly.

Ma. There's a fog tonight. I can smell it.

Tom. (*He stares out of the window.*) There's a fog, all right. Comin' up from the river.

Ma. Raise the window a minute, Son.   Let me listen to Old River.

Tom. All right, Ma.

(*He raises the window to its full height, and we can hear the ROAR of the river in the darkness outside.*)

Ma. (*She half turns her head, suspending her work while she listens.   Then she nods with satisfaction.*) Old River's loud tonight.   Purtiest sight I know, Old River a-rushin' and roarin' in the moonlight.

Tom. (*Closing the window*) No moonlight now.   Won't be moon-up for most an hour.   Too dark out now to see t'other end of a bull calf. (*He crosses to the mantel and picks up his pipe and tobacco.*) Ma, you heerd how loud th' river is!   She's comin' close—too close!   We can't stay in this house no longer.   Ain't safe!

Ma. I ain't a-feared, Tom.   Forty years Old River's been tryin' to git us, eatin' toward us a mite more each freshet time.   But she ain't got us yet, and she won't.

Tom. She will ef'n we don't move out!   Used to be we had two acres of 'taters out there 'tween us and the river.   Corn, too.   But they ain't there now!

Ma. It was five acres when yore Pa built this house. Best 'taters and corn any place hereabouts, too.

Tom. Two acres er five acres, we got to move, and we got to do it soon. (*Persuasive*) Ma, we can move to Gridley's place, down by town.   Gridley wants I should take keer of his stock.   We could have us a house with 'lectric lights and you could get you a rest to the hospital; get you your strength back.

Ma. All right, Son, we'll move.   Allus told yore Pa we'd have to move some day, way Old River kept a-hungerin' for us and eatin' toward us.

Tom. Tomorrow, Ma? You aim we should move to-morrow?

Ma. Not tomorrow, Son. Not till after Harry comes. After yore brother comes. He comes from a long way and he don't never stay long, and ef'n we moved he moughtn't find us. Mought go away again and not find us.

Tom. But Ma! Ain't no tellin' when Harry'll get to come again! River won't wait fer him—won't wait fer nobody!

Ma. (*There is finality in her tone—the finality of the aged, who cannot be argued with.*) When Harry's come back, Tom, when his Ma's got to see him again. Then we can move.

Tom. Well, all right, then—we'll let it go fer now. We can talk about it some more come mornin'.

Ma. (*She is becoming excited.*) Mornin' won't change my mind! I got to be here fer Harry—got to be here where my boy can find his Ma when he comes. He may be needin' me and I got to be here!

Tom. All right, Ma. Anyway, it's bedtime. Let me fix you some hot milk 'fore I wheel you into yore room.

Ma. I don't favor any milk, Tom, but you have somethin'.

Tom. I'll have some coffee. There's some in the pot.

(*He exits up right, pausing to straighten the calendar as he goes out.*)
(Ma *reaches out and fumbles at the radio. She switches it on, then, with an expression of triumph, sits back and picks up her work. In a moment the radio begins to play "barn dance" music.* Ma *nods happily in time to the tune as* Tom *returns with an enameled coffee pot, cup and*

*saucer, sugar bowl and spoon, and can of evaporated milk
on a tray, which he puts on the table.)*

Tom. Ma! You turned on the radio.

Ma. You said the radio box wasn't workin', Tom. But
it is. Workin' fine.

Tom. It's the batteries. They're wore out. (*He starts
to turn it off.*)

Ma. Now, Tom! Don't you turn it off! It's pleasurin'
me, and I ain't heered it a bit all day.

Tom. (*He hesitates, then turns down the volume.*) If I
leave it play, will you let me wheel you inside now?
You can hear it plain in yore room.

Ma. All right, Tom. If you leave it playin'.

Tom. (*Comes around behind her; takes her work and
puts it on the table*) As long as she's music, I'll leave her
play. Ef'n it's just talk, I'll turn her off.

(*He is about to start wheeling her towards the up right
door when* **Ma** *abruptly stops him.*)

Ma. No, Tom, no!

Tom. What is it, Ma?

Ma. It's Harry! It's my boy! He's a-comin'!

Tom. (*Startled*) Harry! What do you mean?

Ma. He's near! He's on his way! I can feel him gettin'
closer! He'll be here 'afore moon-up!

Tom. But he couldn't be comin' here tonight!

Ma. (*Happily certain*) But he be! Ain't I always told
you true, t'other times he came?

Tom. Yes, Ma, but—

Ma. When Harry runned off as a little boy, so your
Pa couldn't whup him, I allus knowed when I was near
the place he was hidin'. It's like somethin' callin'

out inside me. And it's tellin'. me he's comin' closer to me now!

Tom. (*Glances frowningly towards the door left, then back at his mother*) Well, if he's comin', you'd best get rested for him. You can sleep till he gets here.

Ma. (*She still prevents him from wheeling her out.*) In a minute, Son. (*Eagerly hopeful*) Mebbe this time Harry'll stay. Mebbe he won't go off again, like he allus has before. (*Thoughtful now, as she stares into the past*) Allus like Old River, Harry was—allus restless, wantin' to go somewhere he warn't, tryin' to climb from out his proper banks to get some'res else in a hurry. Your Pa, he couldn't unnerstand that—couldn't unnerstand it was the river hummin' an' singin' in Harry's blood made him like he was, so that whuppin' only made things worse.

Tom. (*Gently*) Yes, Ma, I know.

Ma. Hungerin' for the city, Harry was, and city clothes an' city talk. Not like you, Son. (*She pats his hand briefly.*) Harry's got the river in his soul, but you got the hills. A body could allus count on you to stay put—be depended on.

Tom. Yes, Ma. Now you got to get some sleep. (*He wheels her toward the door.*)

Ma. All right, Son. I'll sleep till Harry comes. I'll know when he's here. (*She subsides, drowsy and happy, as they go out up right.*)

(*The door remains partly ajar behind them. For a moment the stage is empty. The radio continues playing. Then the door left opens. Harry slips in, for an instant peers into the darkness, then closes the door soundlessly. He is younger than* Tom, *slighter, quicker. He is dressed in a nondescript suit, a fairly good coat over it, a battered hat*)

*pulled down to his face. For a moment he surveys the room.
Then he turns down his coat collar, puts his hat on the
table, and picks up the coffee pot, which* Tom *has left
untouched. He splashes out a cupful, dumps in sugar, stirs it
hastily and gulps it, all the while maintaining an attitude
of alertness. He looks once towards the door through
which* Tom *and* Ma *have vanished, as if hearing sounds
of them. Then he returns to gulping his coffee, curling his
fingers around the cup as if to warm them. He looks
hungry, weary, cold. He has almost finished the coffee
when the music on the radio ceases. After an instant, a
man's voice is heard.*)

Announcer. We interrupt our program to bring you an
important bulletin! The hunt for Harry Holloway, who
escaped last night from the State Penitentiary after
serving five years of a fifteen year term for robbery and
assault, has shifted to this locality. It is believed by
State authorities that Holloway may be heading for his
home on Big Pebbly River, in the hope of—

(Harry, *holding coffee cup in one hand, swiftly leans toward
radio and turns the dial. The voice is cut off. Then he
turns the dial further, finds music similar to that which
was on before, and leaves it on, in a low volume. He
straightens and turns toward the door right, listening. It
is obvious that he hears something, for he hastily gulps the
rest of the coffee. Then he snatches out a handkerchief,
wipes cup and spoon dry, and puts them back on the table
just as he found them. He hesitates an instant longer,
listening; then swiftly he yanks open a drawer in the center
table, searches it, but does not find what he is looking for.
In great haste he crosses to the chest of drawers, fumbles
inside, and brings out a large old revolver. Having picked
up his hat and wiped the table where it had been, he disappears into the curtained storage alcove up left with the*

revolver. The radio plays on, and as he vanishes Tom *comes into the room with a small bundle of soiled clothes, which he sets down on the floor. Then he turns down both kerosene lamps slightly. After that he crosses to the door left, opens it, looks out, closes it again, and crosses to the telephone. He gives the crank a spin and picks up the receiver.*)

Tom. Hello, Elsie? Give me the Sheriff's office, will you? Thanks— (*As he waits for the connection, automatically he straightens some old newspapers on the chest of drawers.* Harry *stirs behind the curtain; we cannot see him, but we know that he is there.*) Hello —Sheriff's office? Sheriff Dexter there? This is Tom Holloway— Oh—Oh, I see. He left half an hour ago to come here? Fog must have held him up— Yes, I'll tell him soon's he gets here— (*There is the sound of KNOCKING at the front door.* Tom *turns his head, then turns back to the telephone.*) Hang on a moment. Here he is now— (*He lets the receiver hang free and opens the door.*) Come in, Sheriff. I was just callin' yore office. Deputy's on the phone—wants to talk to you.

(Sheriff Dexter *enters. He is a short, burly man, wearing an old mackinaw, a misshapen hat on his head. He has a powerful flashlight in his hand.*)

Sheriff. Mebbe they've nabbed him down the line. Sure hope so. (*He crosses to the telephone, lifts the receiver.*) Hello, Bill. Anything break yet? — Oh, no sign of him?—Well, I'm here at th' house. Got two of my best boys outside. Can't do no more'n that till I get more men—I don't care what th' prison phoned; I ain't God A'mighty— Bloodhounds? Comin' from Stone Mountain?—Be midnight afore they get here. But we'll sure be able to use 'em. Ef'n he gets loose in this valley, ain't no human critters goin' to run him down—

Sure, I'll be keepin' in touch with you. This is where he's aimin' fer an' I'm stickin' around. If my old lady calls, you tell her that. Tell her she'll see me when I get there— 'Bye. (*He hangs up and turns towards* Tom, *putting his gloves, hat, and flashlight on the center table, where, a few minutes before,* Harry's *hat was.*) Shore feel bad about this, Tom. You aint seen no sign of him, have you?

Tom. (*He shakes his head.*) He wouldn't be comin' this way. Too risky.

Sheriff. Hell, man, you mean you ain't heerd?

Tom. Heerd? Heerd what?

Sheriff. He sure is comin' this way! He mought be somewhere around here right this minute. Guess he thumbed a ride—anyway, there was a car found in a ditch couple miles t'other side of the pass, 'bout six o'clock. He could have skinned over the pass and got here by now!

Tom. Then Ma was right! She said he was comin' here tonight!

Sheriff. It's been on the radio all evening that he was headin' this way.

Tom. Had the radio turned off till just now. (*He turns it off again.*) Turned it off first thing this morning, when the news about his escape came over. Didn't want Ma to hear it.

Sheriff. Oh, so that's it. (*Looks around; sits in armchair*) I was plumb worried about you. Phoned three, four times, and couldn't get no answer. Thought mebbe Harry'd got here already.

Tom. (*Crosses to telephone and pulls paper wads from between bells*) Had the phone plugged. Ma can wheel herself over and answer it. Didn't want no gossipy neighbors callin' up to tell her all about her boy Harry.

Sheriff. Then she don't know what Harry's been up to?

Tom. (*Shakes his head*) She don't even know he's been in the penitentiary. Thinks he's been workin' out west all along. Every once in a while I write her a letter, makin' out like it's from Harry, then read it to her when it comes. (*A pause; then:*) Expect it would kill her ef'n ever she found out the truth.

Sheriff. (*Nods soberly and begins to roll himself a home-made cigarette*) Always been extra fond of him, ain't she?

Tom. (*He speaks calmly, without bitterness.*) He was allus her boy. When Pa was layin' to whup him, she'd help him skin out the window there and hide.

Sheriff. I remember— But you said she said he was comin' here tonight! She *must* know about him, then!

Tom. She didn't *know* he was comin'—she felt it. Last time he showed up, she knowed about it an hour ahead.

Sheriff. S'prised he ain't here already. A night like this is made to order for Harry, knowin' the valley like he does.

Tom. How many men you got out?

Sheriff. End of th' valley is sealed up by a posse. I got men up in the pass too. Prob'ly got 'em there too late, though. Got two outside—one up the trail, t'other down. They'll watch all night. But I'm scared Harry may take to the river— You still got your boat tied up down in the gorge?

Tom. Expect I have. You want I should padlock it?

Sheriff. Sink it! Let Harry get to it and he could float right through all the posses in creation, be halfway to hell'n gone by sun-up. Water's high enough. (*He crosses to the window, raises it, and peers out. For a moment we hear again the muted ROAR of the river plunging*

through the gorge outside. After a moment the Sheriff
lowers the window and turns back into the room.) Still
blacker'n the inside of a hound dog—can't see a thing.
Moon-up'll help, though.

Tom. I reckon.

Sheriff. River sounded loud—mighty loud. Gettin'
closer?

Tom. (*He nods.*) Been cavin' the banks again. Ma
won't move, though. Afraid she'll miss Harry when he
comes.

Sheriff. Better talk her around afore next spring freshets
get hungry for this house!

Tom. I'll talk her around. When Harry's caught—

Sheriff. Well?

Tom. Maybe you could let Ma visit him a minute—
'thout lettin' on he's a prisoner? Then she'll be all
right.

Sheriff. Mebbe. Be hard, though. I didn't tell you,
Tom—that car we found in the ditch—

Tom. Yes?

Sheriff. The driver was still in it—his head bashed in
with a wrench.

Tom. No!

Sheriff. Yep! Bashed in like a ripe melon.

Tom. You're sayin' Harry did it? Killed him?

Sheriff. Who else could it've been?

Tom. But Harry ain't a killer! He's done plenty—but
he never murdered in cold blood!

Sheriff. Well, he has now. (*Suddenly suspicious*) Tom—
Harry ain't here now, is he? You ain't hidin' him, are
you?

Tom. (*Shakes his head*) He ain't here. I swear to that.

Sheriff. (*Partly relaxes*) I believe you, Tom. But suppose he gives us all the slip and does show up? What then?

Tom. You think I'd hide out a killer—even my own kin?

Sheriff. Plenty folk around here would. And with your Ma dotin' on him like she does, I ain't so sure.

(*A slight movement of the curtain behind which* Harry *is hiding tells us that he is listening intently.*)

Tom. If he hadn't turned killer—no, I don't rightly know. I won't go for to say. But if he gets here, I'll hold him for you. Only Ma ain't ever to know. She ain't ever to know!

Sheriff. We'll manage it. Just you keep mindin', if he does get here, that helpin' a killer is near as bad in the eyes of the law as bein' one.

Tom. Don't fret about me. But we got to keep Ma from ever knowin' about it.

Sheriff. (*Rising*) We'll do all we rightly can. (*He turns towards the phone.*) Got to call my office.

Tom. (*Crossing to above table*) I'll heat you up some coffee. Got just about a cup left here in the pot. (*He picks up the pot as the* Sheriff *crosses to the phone. He feels that it is empty, and is puzzled.*) Guess I drank it myself. But I'll make up a potful.

Sheriff. Drink it when I get back. Got to check up on my men. Only be about ten minutes. (*He spins telephone crank.*) Mought boil up some fer my men too. Gonna need it 'fore the night's over. Oh—an' don't fergit about that boat!

Tom. Sure, Sheriff. I'll tend to it soon's I've put the coffee on. (*He exits up right with the coffee pot.*)

Sheriff. Hello, Elsie, this is Sheriff Dexter. Give me my office, will you—Hello, Bill? Anything new?—All right, then—I'm stickin' right here. Got a tip he's close by. And listen—when them bloodhounds get there, call me right away—Sure, that's all.

(*He hangs up, picks up his hat and flashlight, and goes out. The door has been closed behind him only for three or four seconds when* Tom *hurries back in, still holding the coffee pot.*)

Tom. Sheriff! (*He sees that the* Sheriff *is gone. For a moment he holds the pot indecisively. Then he sets it on the table and slowly crosses to the chest of drawers. He opens the drawer, fumbles inside for a moment, then brings out a tin of tobacco. He picks up his pipe, and turns towards the hiding place.*) All right, Harry. You mought as well come out.

(*A moment's pause, then* Harry *emerges, casually keeping his right hand in his pocket, where the gun is concealed.*)

Harry. Hello, Tom! Empty coffee pot gave me away, didn't it? (Tom, *fumbling with his pipe and tobacco, his eyes fixed on his brother, only nods.*) Same old Tom! Slow but sure in the upper story! (*Drops into armchair, drapes one leg over an arm, and smiles contemptuously at* Tom) You could at least say hello when your only brother drops in for a visit.

Tom. (*Crosses to above table before he speaks*) Is it true? What the Sheriff said about that driver?

Harry. Sure it's true. I wasn't going to hurt him if he did what I said, but he decided he'd be smart.

Tom. Oh!

Harry. He figured I didn't really have a gun in my pocket—and he was right. But I had a wrench. That's how the car came to go in the ditch. (*He pauses, watch-*

ing Tom.) And that's where I got this topcoat. This other elegant gent's outfit (*He displays the shabby suit beneath the topcoat.*) came from somebody's barn. Along with the hat.

Tom. Why'd you come here?

Harry. To see my dear old Ma, of course. Why else?

Tom. Did you figure we'd help you out of this scrape?

Harry. (*He is watching* Tom *closely.*) Most folks around here help their kin, no matter what the Law wants them for.

Tom. I can't do it, Harry. You heerd what I said to the Sheriff. No, I can't do it.

Harry. (*Sneeringly*) Same old Tom. Can't stand a little killin'! Just like when you used to take a rabbit out of my traps if it was still alive!—Well, I can count on Ma. Where is she?

Tom. She's sleepin'. And she don't know anything about you. She thinks you've been working out in California last five years.

Harry. You mean you never told her her dear boy Harry was locked up in a nasty old penitentiary with a lot of thieves and murderers?

Tom. Nobody's never told her. It would kill her ef'n she found out.

Harry. I never thought you could keep from telling her, seeing how jealous you were of me.

Tom. I wasn't jealous of you, Harry. I was sorry fer you—you wantin' all the things you couldn't have.

Harry. Well, I had 'em, didn't I? Cities and bright lights—two inch steaks and decent liquor—soft beds—pretty girls—I had 'em all! You, sorry for me! Why, I've blown more money on horses and women than you'll see in a lifetime!

Tom.   Not many horses or women in a jailhouse.

Harry.   Why, you—(*He checks himself.*) That was a bad break, that's all! Now listen! I need money and food. I'm going to take your boat and get down the river. Once I hit the South Fork I'm safe—Well, don't just stand there. That damned Sheriff will be coming back. Get a move on!

Tom.   I can't let you go, Harry. You're stayin' here till Sheriff gets back.

Harry.   (*He takes the gun from his pocket.*) If that's the way you feel, it's a good thing I found this in the drawer. Pa's old pistol—loaded, too!

Tom.   It won't do you no good, Harry.

Harry.   I want whatever money you've got and I want some food and I want them quick. (*He rises and half lifts the gun.*)

Tom.   Can't do it, Harry.

Harry.   You think I'm bluffing, do you? You think I won't shoot if I have to?

Tom.   You can't shoot. I'm goin' to walk over and get my gun—and you're not goin' to shoot. (*He turns his back and starts slowly towards the fireplace.*)

Harry.   I warn you—stand still! Stand still, I say! —All right, you asked for it! (*He tries to fire the gun. The trigger will not pull. For an instant he struggles with it, then lowers it, his face terrible.*) Damn you! It won't fire!

Tom.   (*He picks up his rifle and comes back, the gun under his arm but pointing generally at* Harry.) It's rusted. Never been fired since Pa died.

Harry.   No wonder you acted so brave—knowing you weren't going to get hurt.

Tom. I wanted to see would you shoot or not. I—didn't reckon you would.

Harry. Well, now you know!

Tom. Prison's changed you, Harry.

Harry. Well, nothing's changed you. Still a preacher at heart! (*He flings himself back into the chair angrily.*) All right, now what?

Tom. Just wait for the Sheriff. Then we'll fix you up some supper and you'll be going back!

Harry. You're crazy if you think I'm waiting here nice and peaceful for the Sheriff. (*He half rises, watching Tom, his body tense, his eyes glittering.*) I'll make a break for it! Soft-hearted Tom, who hates killing so much, isn't going to shoot his brother!

Tom. (*Bringing up the rifle*) I'll get you in th' leg—ef'n I have to. My aim's good when I got to shoot.

Harry. (*Subsides, but still watches Tom alertly, his voice changes as a new idea comes to him.*) It's going to be an awful disappointment to Ma not to get to talk to me.

Tom. She won't know. She won't ever know you came.

Harry. But suppose she wakes up when the Sheriff comes back?

Tom. She won't. She fell asleep sound.

Harry. I have an idea she'll wake up!

Tom. Why should she? What're you trying to say?

Harry. I mean she'll wake up when she hears me yelling when you and the Sheriff lug me out!

Tom. But then she'd know! About you!

Harry. Yes—then she'd know.

Tom. It would kill her!

Harry. I wouldn't know about that. But I'm sure going to yell.

Tom. You couldn't. You'd be killin' your own Ma. Nobody could be that low.

Harry. I tell you I will. Unless you let me get out that window and down to the boat before the Sheriff gets back.

(*Startled by the idea*, Tom *glances at the window.*)

Tom. Out that window?

Harry. That's what I said! The door's being watched —but I used that window for a getaway plenty of times when Pa was fixing to whup me, and I can use it again now!

Tom. But the river—

Harry. Never mind about the river! It and me, we understand each other. I'll get down the path to the boat, and once I cast off I'm safe. The boat's still there —I heard you say so!

Tom. Yes, it's still there—only it's tied up further down.

Harry. I'll find it! Moon-up'll give me enough light to see by, and if I stay in the shadow close to the cliffs nobody'll see *me*—Well, I've got to be going!

(*He essays rising*, *as if to move towards the window.* Tom *swings the gun up again.*)

Tom. Set still, Harry! (Harry *subsides. There is a KNOCK-ING at the door left.* Tom *turns his head towards it in great relief.*) Come in, Sheriff. Quick!

Sheriff. (*The door opens and the* Sheriff *enters. He has the door partly shut again when he notices the tableau and reacts by reaching for his gun.*) God A'mighty, it's Harry!

Tom. Shet the door, Sheriff. Don't need your gun. He's harmless.

Sheriff. (*Releases his gun and closes the door*) Where'd he come from? How'd he get here?

Tom. He slipped in while I was helpin' Ma to bed, just afore you got here.

Sheriff. This is plumb lucky. I was scared there'd be more killin' before we got him. I'll call my deputies.

Tom. No, Sheriff! Ma might hear you. We got to get him out of here afore she wakes.

Sheriff. That's so, ain't it? Well, just let me get the cuffs on him and I figure we can handle him. Keep him covered, though.

(*He puts his flashlight on the table and brings out a pair of handcuffs, while* Harry *watches alertly.*)

Harry. You think I'm leaving without saying good-bye to my dear old mother? Well, you're wrong! (*He raises his voice.*) Ma! Oh, Ma, where are you?

(Tom *freezes in dismay.* Harry *grins crookedly at him. The* Sheriff, *starting toward* Harry, *pauses.*)

Ma. (*Her voice comes from off.*) Harry? Be that you, Harry?

Harry. It's me all right, Ma! I've come for to see you!

Ma. I knowed you was a-comin', son! Come in here, and bring me out to the light where your Ma can look at you!

Harry. I'll be right in, Ma. Soon's I've said hello to Tom. (*Lowering his voice*) Well, Tom, now she knows I'm here, I expect I just can't go without a little visit with her.

Sheriff. (*Steps forward with the cuffs*) You sure kin, and you're goin' to. Put out yore hands.

Harry. How about it, Tom? Shall I tell her I can't stay because I've got a date with the Sheriff?

(Tom's *features express an agony of indecision.*)

Ma. Harry, Son, what's keepin' you? Your Ma's all a-tremble, just hungerin' to see you. Come bring me out to the light.

Sheriff. I said put out yore hands! I'm not takin' any nonsense!

Tom. No, Sheriff, wait!

Sheriff. Tom, I know you don't want to upset your Ma, but Harry's a killer, and I just can't—

(*He has half turned towards* Tom, *and* Harry *suddenly moves behind the* Sheriff. *He grabs the* Sheriff's *left wrist and swings it up behind the officer's back in a punishing wrist lock. The cuffs remain in the* Sheriff's *left hand. With his right hand* Harry *grabs for the* Sheriff's *gun, but the* Sheriff *clamps his right hand down on the revolver also. For a moment they strain silently, neither able to gain the gun.*)

Sheriff. Tom! Shoot quick! You can wing him!

Harry. Better not, Tom! No matter who you hit, it'd upset Ma!

(Tom *wavers indecisively.*)

Sheriff. Shoot, Tom, shoot!

(*They are still struggling for the gun, only their bodies swaying in the deadlock of their position.*)

Ma. Tom—Tom, what's a-keepin' Harry?

Tom. (*Agonized indecision in his voice*) He'll be in— in just a minute, Ma!

Sheriff. I can't—hold out—much longer. He's breakin' my arm!

Harry. Think fast, Tom! In a second I'll have the gun and somebody will get killed. But give me your promise—let me get safe out that window—and nobody'll be hurt.

Tom. All right, Harry—you got my promise! (*He swings the rifle so that it covers the* Sheriff.) Let go the gun, Sheriff!

Sheriff. Tom, you're plain crazy! He's a killin' varmint!

Tom. Let go the gun!

(Harry *gives a final wrench to the* Sheriff's *arm, and the officer, twisting with pain, lets* Harry *take the gun.* Harry *releases him and stands back, gun leveled. The* Sheriff *rubs his arm and stares at* Tom.)

Sheriff. Tom, you're earnin' a big prison sentence for yourself.

Tom. Take it easy, Sheriff. Put yore hands behind yore back. Harry, put the cuffs on him.

(*Slowly the* Sheriff *gives in.* Harry *hesitates an instant, then jams the gun in his pocket, grabs the* Sheriff's *arms, and forces them brutally behind his back. He fastens the handcuffs, then steps back, his hand near the gun in his pocket, watching* Tom.)

Harry. How does it feel, Sheriff? Now you know what it's like!

Tom. Now go get Ma, Harry. Bring her in here, like she wants. You got to ease her mind before you go.

Harry. All right, Tom. (*Mocking*) Now you're acting like a real brother.

Ma. Harry, Harry boy! Why don't you come?

Harry. Coming, Ma. Coming now. (*He crosses up right and exits.*)

Sheriff. Tom, you know what you're doin'? You're aidin' a killer. You're makin' yourself accessory to murder!

Tom.   I'm doin' what I got to do, Sheriff.

Sheriff.   You're not figurin' I'm goin' to be easy on you? Because I ain't, Tom.

Tom.   Whatever you got to do, I won't try to stop you. But I can't do different now.

Sheriff.   He ain't fitten to live! He'd have killed all of us to get away, ef'n he could of managed it!

Tom.   (*Nods heavily*) I expect he would. That's why I got to let him go the way he wants. Now, Sheriff, I could gag you—but if you give me yore promise to be quiet, I won't.

Sheriff.   All right—you got it. Deputies are too far away to hear me, or I'd 'a' yelled afore this.

Tom.   Then you stay put in the storage room till he's gone. After that I'll unlock those cuffs.

Sheriff.   (*Backs toward curtain up left*)   All right, Tom. I'll stay quiet. But afterwards you're reckonin' with me.

(*He disappears behind curtains.* Tom *closes and adjusts curtain.* Harry *re-enters, pushing* Ma *in her wheel chair. She is radiantly happy.*)

Ma.   Tom, he came! I told you he was a-comin', and he came!

Harry.   (*Wheeling her to right of table*) Sure I did.   Don't I always come back to see my old Ma?

Ma.   Yes, Son. But it was a mighty long time. (*She clings to him.*) Tell me you're goin' to stay this time! Tell me you are, Son!

Harry.   Ma, not this time. I can't.

Ma.   Harry, you're not goin' away again tonight? Not right away, when you've just come!

Harry. (*Nods*) Got to, Ma. Some friends are— looking for me. But pretty soon I'll be sending for you. To come stay with me in California.

Ma. Soon, Harry? You'll be sending fer me soon?

Harry. In just a month or two, Ma. You'll love it there. The sun shines all the time in California.

(Tom *stands near the* Sheriff's *hiding place, gun held inconspicuously.*)

Ma. (*Dreamy; she begins to grow sleepy now as* Harry *talks.*) Californy. Tell me about Californy, Son.

Harry. It's a grand place, Ma. It's all covered with farms where they grow oranges. Only they call them ranches. Orange ranches.

Ma. Then you've settled down, Son? Settled down at last?

Harry. That's right, Ma. I'm finished with roaming around. And you're going to come out and live with me. The sun shines warm all day long, winter and summer. The orange trees just bust out all over with fruit. All you have to do is reach out and pick them.

Ma. (*Sleepy, her eyes close for a moment; then she opens them again.*) Go on, Son, tell me more about it. Be there any hills?

Harry. Hills! They got the biggest hills in California that ever was raised up. In the back of my orange ranch the hills reach right up to the sky, all blue and purple, with white snow on the tops.

Ma. (*Nods; her eyes shut*) Sound just like the promised land. Sunshine—warm all around the year—oranges for the pickin'—mountains standin' tall like the glory of God—Go on about Californy, Son.

Harry. There's the mountains, Ma. Then my thousand acres of orange trees, all rolling and green just like a lawn underneath the trees. Then down on the other side is the ocean—the Pacific.

Ma. (*Almost asleep*) The ocean. I've never seed an ocean.

Harry. This is the biggest ocean there is. And the bluest. And the sand on the beach is the whitest. The ocean stretches right off to China on the other side of the world. (Ma *nods contentedly.*) And the waves come in, big blue waves that have traveled all the way from China, and they bring a breeze with them that smells of tea and spice and ginger and cinnamon. The waves break on the beach and it's like thunder way off, or Pebbly River in flood when she's caving in her banks and the big chunks are falling in. And all you'll have to do, Ma, is sit there in the sunshine and soak up strength. And there's the mountains to look at on one side, and the orange ranch all green and gold right in front of you, and the ocean on beyond, with the waves breaking, and the sea gulls crying, and the breeze bringing you all the smells of China and India—(Ma *has stopped nodding. She is asleep now, smiling a little, happily.* Harry *breaks off and straightens cautiously.*) She's asleep, Tom.

Tom. (*Comes forward*) She won't wake up if we're quiet. All right, Harry, you can go now ef'n you want to.

Harry. (*He turns up his coat collar and puts on his hat.*) Still black as pitch out. I'll be needing a light.

Tom. (*He looks towards the table.*) There's the Sheriff's.

Harry. (*Takes it, tries it, thrusts it into his pocket; he nods towards the* Sheriff's *hiding place.*) You got to keep him here till I get safe down to the South Fork, understand?

Tom. (*He nods.*) I'll keep him here till you're beyond catchin', Harry.

Harry. You'd better! (*He takes the gun from his pocket, spins the cylinder, and puts it back. Then he goes to the window, thrusts it to its full height, and inserts a stick to hold it in place. For a moment he turns back to face* Tom.) Moon's readying to clear the peak, so I'm going now, while it's still good and dark. And nobody's stopping me this side of he !

Tom. (*Crossing* *t him*) Harry, don't do it! Stay an' take yore trial! I'll get you the best lawyer in the State!

Harry. What a preacher you'd have made! (*He straddles the sill, gets both legs outside, and prepares to push himself off into the darkness. For an instant he turns toward* Tom; *mockingly*) So long, brother Tom! (*He pushes himself outward, and vanishes.*)

(Tom *stands for a long moment, staring at the empty window. He does not move until the* Sheriff *emerges and comes over to him.* Ma *still sleeps.*)

Sheriff. Well, he's gone! Now you goin' to unlock these cuffs, or you goin' to make it worse for yourself by givin' him a headstart?

Tom. I'll free you, Sheriff.

Sheriff. Key's in my right coat pocket.

(Tom *finds the key and the* Sheriff *turns around. In silence the handcuffs are removed.* Tom *hands them to the* Sheriff; *tries to speak, but cannot. Abruptly he turns and drops to his knees beside his mother's wheel chair. He buries his head in her lap. Through the window, which is wide open, comes now the first glimmer of* MOONLIGHT, *which grows steadily to a strong glow in the feebly lighted room.*)

Tom. Ma! Ma, I had to do it!

(*The* Sheriff *jams the handcuffs into his pocket and crosses to the telephone as* Ma *wakes, blinks, and smiles down at* Tom. *Gently she touches him.*)

Ma. Harry's gone, ain't he, Tom?

Tom. Yes, he's gone. Ma, I couldn't help myself. I had to do it!

Sheriff. (*Spins the crank and speaks into the mouthpiece*) Hello, Elsie! This is Sheriff Dexter! Gimme my office, quick!

Ma. Now don't you fret, Tom. Look—it's moon-up! Harry'll have light for his trip—he won't have to travel in the dark.

Sheriff. (*Impatient*) Well, keep ringin' 'em, Elsie! There's got to be somebody there, damn it! (*He is watching* Tom *and* Ma *as he speaks.*)

Ma. Harry's going to send fer me real soon, Tom. He said so. But up till he does, we can live over by town ef'n you want. We'll fool Old River. We'll move first thing tomorrow. She'll never get a one of us, even though she has undercut right up to the house.

(Tom's *shoulders shake with dry sobs, which are muffled in her lap. He does not answer, but the* Sheriff, *watching them and listening, looks startled.*)

Sheriff. Undercut right up to the house? (*He hastily hangs up the receiver and crosses to the window; leans out and looks downward in the moonlight*)

(Tom *continues kneeling at his mother's side, head buried in her lap, and she strokes his hair, her face lit up with the happiness of her visit with* Harry, *and his promise. After a long moment the* Sheriff *straightens and turns back into the room, staring at* Tom *in dawning understanding.*)

Sheriff. Great God A'mighty! No ground at all left outside now! Just the river an' the rocks—a hundred foot drop straight down from the window!

He looks at Ma *and* Tom. *They do not seem to hear him as moonlight suffuses the room and*

THE CURTAIN FALLS

The Old Lady Shows Her Medals

by J. M. BARRIE

CHARACTERS

Mrs. Dowey
Mrs. Mickleham
Mrs. Haggerty
Mrs. Tully
The Rev. Mr. Wilkinson
Private K. Dowey *of the*
Black Watch

SCENE ONE *is Mrs. Dowey's living-room in a London base-ment in the afternoon.*

SCENE TWO *is the same. Five days later, at night.*

SCENE THREE *is the same. A month or two later, in the early morning.*

THE OLD LADY SHOWS HER MEDALS

SCENE ONE

A basement in a drab locality in London; the kitchen, sitting-room and bedroom of Mrs. Dowey, *the charwoman. It is a poor room, as small as possible but clean and tidy; not at all bare, but containing many little articles and adornments.*

The door to the area is up left. The door to a small scullery is in the right wall rather up stage, below which is a small kitchen grate.

In the left wall is a piece of furniture with the appearance of a cheap wardrobe, but which is, in fact, a bed which can be let down. Below this is a small chest of drawers.

There is a shabby deal table, its length across the stage, set right centre, with two wooden chairs above it and one at each end.

The time is about 5 p.m.

The Curtain *rises on* Mrs. Dowey *entertaining three other charwomen to tea. She is on the right of the table. On her left, above the table is* Mrs. Mickleham, *on whose left is* Mrs. Tully. Mrs. Haggerty, *the unpopular one, is at the left end of the table.*

There is no tablecloth, but there is tea, bread and butter, a dish of shrimps, of which only two are left, jam, and winkles— even a small sponge cake. The loaf and two cut slices are near the hostess. The remaining shrimps, it is noted, are within easy reach of Mrs. Haggerty.

There is a cheerful fire, and the kettle steams on the hob.

All the ladies are elderly, typical, without exaggeration of

145

their profession. Mrs. Mickleham, whose cap and shawl are on a chair above the bed, is the plump one. Mrs. Haggerty, whose things are on the chair up right, is small and rather pathetic. Mrs. Tully, apt to be aggressive, wears her shabby hat, an old coat over the back of her chair.

Mrs. Dowey *has a pale brave face; a Scotswoman who has made a fine struggle against poverty in London.*

It is wartime, and the conversation fluctuates between military strategy and dress fashions.

Mrs. Dowey *stands right, re-filling the teapot with hot water.*

Mrs. Dowey. (*Crossing back to the table*) Another cup of tea, Mrs. Mickleham? (Mrs. Mickleham *waves the offer away.*) Mrs. Haggerty?

Mrs. Haggerty. No, I thank you, I've had so much tea I'm fair running over.

(*Looks of disapproval*)

Mrs. Dowey. Another winkle?

Mrs. Haggerty. If I took one more winkle it'd have to swim for it.

Mrs. Dowey. (*To* Mrs. Tully) The shrimps are with you, Sarah. There's two yet.

Mrs. Tully. Two shrimps yet? There's twelve yet.

Mrs. Haggerty. (*Feeling this is meant for her*) How d'you make that out, ma'am?

Mrs. Tully. (*Who has been nursing a grievance*) There's these two, Mrs. Haggerty, and there's the five *you* had, and the four Mrs. Mickleham had, and the *one* I had.

Mrs. Mickleham. But they're eaten.

Mrs. Tully. (*After a glance at* Mrs. Haggerty) In Germany, Mrs. Mickleham, when a shrimp is eaten, is that the end of the shrimp?

(Mrs. Mickleham *nods approval of this thrust.*)

Mrs. Haggerty. It may be so.

Mrs. Tully. I suppose I ought to know, me that has a son a prisoner in Germany. (*Rather bumptiously*) Being the only lady present that has that proud misfortune.

(*They are humiliated for a moment. Then:*)

Mrs. Dowey. My son's fighting in France.

Mrs. Mickleham. Mine is wounded in two places.

Mrs. Haggerty. Mine is at *Salonikkey.*

(*The* Others *look at her, and she is annoyed.*)

Mrs. Dowey. (*Firmly but not unkindly*) You'll excuse us, Mrs. Haggerty, but the correct pro*noun*ciation is Salo*nikey.*

Mrs. Haggerty. I don't think. (*With a little more spirit than usual*) And I speak as one that has War Savings Certificates.

Mrs. Tully. We all have them.

(*They disdain* Mrs. Haggerty, *and she whimpers.*)

Mrs. Dowey. (*To restore cheerfulness*) Oh, it's a terrible war. (*General chorus of:* "It is." "You may say so.") The men is splendid, but I'm none so easy about the staff. That's your weak point, Mrs. Mickleham.

Mrs. Mickleham. (*Instantly on the defensive*) What none of you grasp is that this is a h'artillery war. Now—

Mrs. Haggerty. I say the word is Salo*nikk*ey.

(*Having surreptitiously eaten the final shrimps, she is strengthened. But the* Others *only display disgust at her ignorance.*)

Mrs. Tully. We'll change the subjeck. (*She takes a magazine from the front of her dress.*) Have you seen this

week's "Fashion Chat"? (All *very attentive*) The plain
smock has come in again with the silk lacing, giving
that charming *cheek* effect.

Mrs. Dowey. Oho! I must say I was always partial
to the straight line—though trying to them as is of too
friendly a figure. (*Her eye considers briefly* Mrs. Mickleham's *want of "line."* Mrs. Mickleham *is resentfully
conscious of this and listens earnestly to* Mrs. Tully's *next*.)

Mrs. Tully. (*Reading*) "Lady Dolly Kinley was seen
conversing across the railings in a dainty *de jou*."

Mrs. Mickleham. (*Eating*) Was she now?

Mrs. Tully. "She is equally popular as maid, wife,
mother, and munition worker." (*Great approval*)
"Lady Pops Babington was married in a tight tulle."

Mrs. Haggerty. (*Fortified by stolen sugar*) What was
her going-away dress?

Mrs. Tully. (*Rolling it out*) "A champagny cream
velvet with dreamy corsage. She's married to Colonel
the Honourable Chingford.—'Snubs' they called him
at Eton."

Mrs. Haggerty. Very likely he'll be sent to Salo*nik*key.

Mrs. Mickleham. Wherever he's sent, she'll have
the same tremors as the rest of us. She'll be as keen to
get the letters wrote in pencil as you or me.

Mrs. Tully. Them pencil letters!

Mrs. Dowey. (*Timidly*) And women in enemy lands
gets those pencil letters—and then stops getting them,
the same as ourselves—let's sometimes think of that.

(*The* Ladies *gasp. Chairs are pushed back*.)

Mrs. Tully. I've heard of females that have no male
relations, and so have no man-party at the war. I've
heard of them—but I don't mix with them.

Mrs. Mickleham. What can the likes of us have to say to them? It's not *their* war.

Mrs. Dowey. They are to be pitied.

Mrs. Mickleham. But the place for them, Mrs. Dowey, is within the doors with the blinds down.

Mrs. Dowey. (*Hurriedly*) Ay, that's the place for them.

Mrs. Mickleham. I saw one of them to-day, buying a flag. I thought it was very impudent of her.

Mrs. Dowey. (*Meekly*) So it was.

Mrs. Mickleham. (*Preening herself and looking at the* Others) I had a letter from my son Percy to-day.

Mrs. Tully. (*Not to be outdone*) Alfred sent me his photo.

Mrs. Haggerty. Letters from Salo*nikk*ey is less common.

(*A general display of pride except from* Mrs. Dowey, *who doggedly sets her lips*)

Mrs. Dowey. Kenneth writes to me every week. (*Exclamations of incredulity; she rises, and crosses left.*) I'll show you. (*She takes a packet of letters, tied up, from the chest of drawers.*) Look at this. All his.

(Mrs. Haggerty *who, behind her hostess's back has just taken and eaten another piece of sugar, whimpers.*)

Mrs. Mickleham. My word!

Mrs. Tully. Alfred has little time for writing, being a bombardier.

Mrs. Dowey. (*Left centre*) Do your letters begin "Dear Mother"?

Mrs. Tully. Generally.

Mrs. Mickleham. Invariable.

Mrs. Haggerty. Every time.

Mrs. Dowey.   Kenneth's begin—"*Dearest* Mother."

(*Speechless, their eyes follow her as she goes up to right centre and fetches a little tray from a small table.*)

Mrs. Tully.   A short man, I should say, judging by yourself.

Mrs. Dowey.   (*Coming down to right end of the table*) Six feet two—and a half.

(*The* Others *are depressed.*)

Mrs. Haggerty.   A kilty, did you tell me?

Mrs. Dowey.   (*Smiling*) Most certainly. He's in the famous Black Watch.

Mrs. Haggerty.   (*Tearful*) The Surrey Rifles is the famousest.

Mrs. Mickleham.   (*Pushing her plate away and leaning forward*) There, you and the King disagree, Mrs. Haggerty. The King's choice is the Buffs—same as my Percy's.

Mrs. Tully.   (*Sitting back, complacent*) Give me the R.H.A., and you can keep the rest.

Mrs. Dowey.   (*Putting plates and cups on the tray*) I'm sure I've nothing to say against the Surreys (*This to* Mrs. Haggerty)—nor the R.H.A. (*To* Mrs. Tully)—nor the Buffs (*To* Mrs. Mickleham; *she lifts the filled tray.*) —but they're all three just breeches regiments, I understand.

Mrs. Haggerty.   We can't all be kilties.

Mrs. Dowey.   (*With satisfaction*) That's verra true.

(*She takes the tray up to the little table.*)

Mrs. Tully.   (*Trying again*) Has your Kenneth great hairy legs?

Mrs. Dowey. (*Coming back to right of the table*) Enormous.

(*The depression deepens.*)

Mrs. Haggerty. (*Rising, speaks across the table*) At any rate it's Salo*nikk*ey. (*She goes up to the window at the back and glances out, then sees someone is descending the steps.*) Ho ho!

(*The* Others *turn to look at her.*)

Mrs. Tully. Who is it, Mrs. Haggerty?

Mrs. Haggerty. (*Moving right*) It's the Reverent gent.

(*There is instant movement. They rise, Mrs. Dowey moves down right, Mrs. Mickleham to above her chair, Mrs. Tully to left of the table. All tidy themselves, smooth hair, etc.*
There is a knock at the door, but the visitor enters at once. It is the Rev. Mr. Wilkinson, *a curate. He is a very good fellow, to whom every little incident in which he figures is of astounding importance. He imparts any information with an air of profound secrecy.*)

Wilkinson. (*Up left*) Quite a party! (*Mrs. Tully offers a chair, dusting it with her apron, forestalling Mrs. Dowey, who had moved to do the same. Mr. Wilkinson waves the chair aside.*) Thank you—not at all. (*Glowing with the surprise in store*) Friends, I have news!

(*All are instantly anxious. Mrs. Haggerty moves down a step.*)

Mrs. Mickleham. (*Coming to back of the table*) News?

Mrs. Haggerty. From the Front?

Mrs. Tully. (*A step towards Mr. Wilkinson*) My Alfred, sir?

Wilkinson. (*With a calming gesture*)   I tell you at once, all's well. (*General relief*) The news— (*With an air*) is for Mrs. Dowey.

Mrs. Dowey. (*Who is really a lonely soul, is thunder-struck*)   News? For me?

Wilkinson. (*With triumph*)   Your son, Mrs. Dowey —he has got five days leave! (*She wets her lips, unable to speak, and lays the letter on left end of the table. The Others all look at her, pleased, if a little envious.*)   Now, now! Good news doesn't kill.

Mrs Tully. (*Sincerely*)   We're glad, Mrs. Dowey.

Mrs. Dowey. (*Moving a pace left, speaks directly to Mr. Wilkinson*)   You're sure?

Wilkinson.   Quite sure.   He has arrived!

Mrs. Dowey.   He's in London?

Wilkinson.   He is.   I have spoken to him.

Mrs. Mickleham. (*To Mrs. Dowey*)   You lucky!

Mrs. Dowey. (*To Wilkinson*)   Where?

Wilkinson. (*Up to Mrs. Tully*)   Ladies, it's quite a romance! I was in the— (*He glances round cautiously before continuing.*) in the Church Army quarters in Central Street, trying to get on the track of one or two of our missing men, when—suddenly, I can't account for it— my eyes alighted on a Highlander seated rather drearily on a bench with his kit at his feet.

Mrs. Haggerty. (*Anxiously, approaching right end of the table*)   A big man?

Wilkinson.   A great brawny fellow. (Mrs. Haggerty *sighs and turns away.*) "My friend," I said at once, "welcome back to Blighty!" I make a point of calling it Blighty. "I wonder," I said, "if there is anything I can do for you?" He shook his head. "What regiment?'' I asked. "Black Watch, Fifth Battalion," he said. "Name?" I asked. (*A slight pause*) "Dowey!" says he. (*Triumphantly*) "Kenneth Dowey," I said, "I know your mother."

Mrs. Haggerty. I declare! I do declare!

Mrs. Dowey. (*Quietly, again wetting her lips*) What did he say to that?

Wilkinson. He was incredulous. Indeed, he seemed to think I was balmy. But I offered to bring him straight to you. I told him how much you had talked to me about him.

Mrs. Dowey. (*Almost in a whisper*) Bring him here?

Mrs. Mickleham. I wonder he needed to be brought.

Wilkinson. He had just arrived, and was bewildered in the great city. He listened to me in his taciturn Scotch way, and then he gave a curious laugh.

Mrs. Tully. Laugh?

Wilkinson. (*Turning to her*) The Scottish, Mrs. Tully, express their emotions differently from us. With them, tears signify a rollicking mood, while merriment denotes that they are plunged in gloom. When I had finished, he said, "Let's go and see the old lady."

Mrs. Dowey. (*Picking up the letters without glancing down, backs a step*) Is he—coming?

Wilkinson. He *has* come! He is up there!

Mrs. Mickleham. (*Goes to the window*) My word!

(*The other two guests follow her.*)

Wilkinson. (*Moving towards* Mrs. Dowey) I told him I thought I had better break the joyful news to you.

Mrs. Dowey. (*In a low, urgent voice*) Get them away.

(*She goes down left, to the chest of drawers.*)

Wilkinson. (*Turning up to the* Others) Ladies, I think this happy occasion scarcely requires *us*. (*They nod acquiescence.*) I don't mean to stay, myself.

(Mrs. Mickleham *goes to the chair above the bed for her cap and shawl and pail.*)

Mrs. Tully. (*Putting on her coat and cap*) I would thank none for their company if my Alfred was at the door. (*She goes up to the door with the pail.*) A noble five days to you, Mrs. Dowey.

(Mrs. Haggerty *has fetched her things from the chair above the fire.*)

Mrs. Haggerty. (*To right of* Mrs. Tully) The same from me.

Mrs. Tully. (*To* Wilkinson) Shall I send him down, sir?

Wilkinson. Yes, do! Do!

(*Exit* Mrs. Tully *and* Mrs. Haggerty)

Mrs. Mickleham. Look at the poor joyous thing, sir. She has his letters in her hand.

(*She exits after the* Others.)

Wilkinson. (*Coming down a little*) A good son to have written to you so often, Mrs. Dowey. (*The letters slip from her hand to the floor. He picks them up and gives them back.*) There! There! (Dowey *is seen descending the steps outside. He enters up left. He is a big grim fellow in field service kit, with kilt, bonnet, overcoat, scarf, etc., of the Black Watch. They are muddy. He carries pack and rifle. He is a dour-looking fellow at present. Up to left of* Dowey, *who is up centre*) Dowey, there she is, waiting for you with your letters in her hand.

Dowey. (*Grimly*) That's great! (Mr. Wilkinson *goes off consciously and stealthily, without looking behind him. He closes the door and is seen to ascend the steps, and off.* Dowey *surveys* Mrs. Dowey, *lowering the butt of his rifle. She backs a pace or two timidly.*) Do you recognize your loving son, Missis? (*He puts his rifle against the chair above the bed and comes to centre, on the left of the table.*) I'm pleased I wrote to ye so often. (*Roughly*) Let's see them. (*Stepping to her, he takes the letters from her hand, and returns centre. She moves a pace nearer him. He pulls off the ribbon and examines the letters.*) Nothing but blank paper! Is this your writing on the envelopes? (*She can only nod.*) The covey told me you were a charwoman, so I suppose you picked the envelopes out of waste-paper baskets, and then changed the address—them being written in pencil. (*She nods again.*) Hah! (*He strides above the table to the fire. She follows him quickly below the table, on his left.*)

Mrs. Dowey. Don't you burn them letters, Mister!

Dowey. (*Staying his hand*) They're not real letters.

Mrs. Dowey. They're all I have.

Dowey. (*Ironically*) I thought you had a son?

Mrs. Dowey. (*Turning her face from him a little*) I never had a son, nor a husband, nor anything. I just call myself Missis to give me a standing.

Dowey. (*Amazed*) Well, it's past my understanding. (*He throws the letters on the table.*) What made you do it?

Mrs. Dowey. It was everybody's war except mine. I wanted it to be my war too.

Dowey. You'll need to be plainer—

Mrs. Dowey. Well—I—

Dowey. (*Crossing back above the table*) And yet I'm d—d if I care to hear, you lying old trickster! (*He goes to the rifle left and picks it up.*)

Mrs. Dowey. (*Following him, to left end of the table*) You're not going already?

Dowey. Yes. I just came to give you a piece of my mind.

Mrs. Dowey. (*With a little begging gesture*) You haven't given it to me yet.

(*He gives a short, hard laugh. His rifle butt thuds on the floor.*)

Dowey. You have a cheek! (*He stares at her.*)

Mrs. Dowey. You wouldn't—drink some tea? (*She goes right towards the fire.*)

Dowey. (*Following her to left end of the table*) Me! I tell you I came here for the one purpose of blazing away at you!

Mrs. Dowey. (*Putting the kettle on the hob*) You could drink the tea while you was blazing away. (*With a nod at the table*)

Dowey. (*Interested*) Not me. You're just a common rogue. (*He sits in* Mrs. Tully's *chair about a yard left of the table.*) Now then, out with it! (*He roars.*) Sit down! (*She returns to right of the table.*) Although it's on your knees you should be to me.

Mrs. Dowey. I'm willing.

Dowey. Stop it! (*She sits, and fingers the letters.*) **Go** on, you accomplished liar.

Mrs. Dowey. It's true that my name is Dowey.

Dowey. It's enough to make me change mine.

Mrs. Dowey. I've been charring and charring and

charring as far back as I mind. I've been in London this twenty years.

Dowey. (*Moving restlessly*) We'll skip your early days. I've an appointment.

Mrs. Dowey. And then, when I was old, the war broke out.

Dowey. How could it affect you?

Mrs. Dowey. (*Rising, she speaks with slow hesitation.*) Oh, Mister, that's the thing. It didn't affect me. It affected everybody *but* me. The neighbours looked down on me. Even the posters on the walls, of the woman saying, "Go, my boy", leered at me. I sometimes cried by myself in the dark. (*She moves tentatively to the hob.*) You won't have a cup of tea?

Dowey. No.

Mrs. Dowey. Sudden-like, the idea came to me to pretend I had a son.

Dowey. You nasty old limmer! But what in the name of old Nick made you choose *me* out of the whole British Army?

Mrs. Dowey. (*With a sly chuckle, she approaches him.*) Maybe, Mister, it was because I liked you best.

Dowey. (*Sitting up, sharply*) Now, now, woman!

Mrs. Dowey. I read one day in the papers, "In which he was assisted by Private K. Dowey, 5th Battalion, Black Watch."

Dowey. (*Flattered*) Did you now? Well, I expect that's the only time I was ever in the papers.

Mrs. Dowey. (*Quickly*) But I didn't choose you for that alone.

Dowey. Eh?

Mrs. Dowey. I read a history of the Black Watch first to make sure it was the best regiment in the world.

Dowey. (*Complacently*) Anybody could have told you that. (*He rises, to the table, on her left; almost unconsciously he picks up a loaf.*) I like the voice of you. (*Unthinkingly he is cutting a slice.*) It drummles on like a Scotch burn.

Mrs. Dowey. Brosen Water runs by where I was born. Maybe it learned me to speak, Mister.

(*He looks at her sharply. Then, evasively:*)

Dowey. Oh, havers!

Mrs. Dowey. (*Sitting right end of the table*) I read about the Black Watch's ghostly piper, that plays proudly when the men of the Black Watch do well, and still prouder when they fall.

Dowey. (*Pleased*) Ay, there's some foolish story of the kind. (*He looks at her.*) But you couldn't have been living here at the time, or they would have guessed. (*He carelessly butters the slice.*) I suppose you changed your place of residence?

Mrs. Dowey. Ay! It cost eleven and six-pence.

Dowey. (*Puts down the slice*) How did you guess that the "K" in my name stood for Kenneth?

Mrs. Dowey. Does it? (*He nods.*) An angel whispered it to me in my sleep.

Dowey. (*Picks up the buttered slice and comes down below the table*) That's the only angel in the whole black business. (*He crosses to the fireplace.*) You little thought I would turn up. (*He swings round sharply.*) Or did you?

Mrs. Dowey. (*Rising, moves above the table, not looking at him*) I was wearying for a sight of you— (*She looks down at the table.*) Kenneth.

Dowey. (*Who was about to take a bite, checks*) What word was that?

Mrs. Dowey. (*Humbly correcting herself*) —Mister.

Dowey. (*Sarcastically*) I hope you're pleased with me now you see me. (*He takes a bite of bread.*)

Mrs. Dowey. (*Earnestly*) I'm very pleased. (Dowey *sits right of the table. She pushes the jam-pot to him.*)

Dowey. No, thank you.

(*Disappointed,* Mrs. Dowey *turns away left. An idea strikes her and she goes left to the chest of drawers and brings out the cash-box, returning to centre.*)

Mrs. Dowey. Look, I have five War Savings Certificates.

Dowey. (*Munching*) That's nought to me.

Mrs. Dowey. I'll soon have six.

Dowey. (*Dourly*) What care I?

Mrs. Dowey. You're hard.

Dowey. I am.

(*She goes back left and returns the cash-box to the drawer, then comes back to left of the table.*)

Mrs. Dowey. Does your folk live in Scotland?

Dowey. (*Unconsciously spreading jam on the bread*) Glasgow.

Mrs. Dowey. Both living?

Dowey. Uh huh.

Mrs. Dowey. Is your mother terrible proud of you?

Dowey. Naturally.

Mrs. Dowey. You'll be going to them?

Dowey. After I've had a skite in London first.

Mrs. Dowey. (*With a little sniff*) So she's in London?

Dowey. Who?

Mrs. Dowey.   Your young lady.

Dowey.   Are you jealous?

Mrs. Dowey.   (*Haughtily*)   Not me!

Dowey.   (*Reaching out for more jam*)   You needna. *She's* a young thing.

Mrs. Dowey.   (*Sarcastic*)   You surprise me. A beauty, no doubt?

Dowey.   Famous. (*Swallowing a mouthful*)   She's a titled person. Her picture's in all the papers. She is equally popular as maid, wife, mother, and munition worker.

Mrs. Dowey.   (*Remembering*)   Oh!

Dowey.   She's sent me a lot of things—especially cakes, and a worsted waistcoat—with a loving message on the enclosed card.

Mrs. Dowey.   (*Coming to above left end of the table*) Do you know her?

Dowey.   Only in the illustrations. But she may have seen me.

Mrs. Dowey.   You'll try one of my cakes. (*She goes towards the scullery.*)

Dowey.   Not me.

(Mrs. Dowey *goes into the scullery, returning at once with a plate of small cakes. They should be of unusual appearance. She puts them on the table within his reach.*)

Mrs. Dowey.   They're my own making.

Dowey.   (*Looking sharply at them*)   Well, I'm d—d!

Mrs. Dowey.   How?

Dowey.   That's exactly the same kind of cake that her ladyship sends me.

Mrs. Dowey. (*In her glory*) Is the waistcoat right? (*He pushes away his plate.*) I hope the Black Watch colours pleased you, Mister.

Dowey. (*Rising*) Wha-at? Was it you?

Mrs. Dowey. (*For the moment a little scared again*) I dared not give my own name, you see, and everyone's familiar with hers.

Dowey. (*Backing a little right*) Woman! Is there no getting rid of you?

Mrs. Dowey. (*Her courage returning*) Are you angry?

Dowey. Oh, hell! Give me some tea. (*He sits at the table again.*)

(Mrs. Dowey *hurries happily into the scullery, returning at once with duplicate teapot with tea ready made, and a cup and saucer. The latter she puts on the table. The teapot she takes to the hob; business of pouring hot water in; during this* Dowey *has been eating.*)

Mrs. Dowey. (*Putting the teapot in front of him*) Kenneth!

Dowey. (*This time he does not notice the use of his name.*) What?

Mrs. Dowey. Nothing. Just—Kenneth. (*She fetches a large cup from the table up stage.*)

Dowey. (*Between bites*) Now don't you be thinking, Missis, for one moment that you've got me.

Mrs. Dowey. (*Busy with milk and sugar*) No, no.

Dowey. (*Spreading jam*) I have a theatre to-night, followed by a randy-dandy.

Mrs. Dowey. Have you? (*She pours out his tea.*) Kenneth, this is a queer first meeting. (*She hands him a cup.*)

Dowey. It is. (*Stirring the tea*) And it's also a last meeting. (*He pours tea into the saucer.*) Ave atque vale. (*He drinks.*) That means, hail and farewell.

Mrs. Dowey. (*Sitting on right chair above the table*) Are you a scholar?

Dowey. Being Scottish, there's almost nothing I don't know.

Mrs. Dowey. What was your trade?

Dowey. (*Reaching out for the loaf*) Carter, glazier, orra man, any rough jobs.

Mrs. Dowey. You're a proper man to look at.

Dowey. (*Cutting another slice*) I'm generally admired.

Mrs. Dowey. (*Rising*) She's an enviable woman.

Dowey. Who?

Mrs. Dowey. Your mother. (*Up to the small table*)

Dowey. Eh? Oh! That was just protecting myself from you. (*She turns, a small cup and saucer in her hand, and looks at him, very still.*) I have neither father nor mother nor wife nor grandmamma. (*She brings the cup down to the table. He continues bitterly.*) This party never even knew who his proud parents were.

Mrs. Dowey. (*Excited*) Is that true?

Dowey. It's Gospel.

Mrs. Dowey. Heavens be praised! (*She pours herself a cup of tea.*)

Dowey. Eh? None of that! I was a fool to tell you. But don't think you can take advantage of it. Pass the cake.

Mrs. Dowey. (*Bringing cake to him, peeps at his legs*) Hairy legs!

Dowey. (*Jocularly, covering his legs with his coat*) Mind your manners. (*Drinking to her*) But here's to you.

Mrs. Dowey. (*Raising her cup*) Here's to you. (*She drinks; then slyly*) And our next meeting.

Dowey. I canna guess where that's to be.

Mrs. Dowey. Maybe in Berlin.

Dowey. Gosh! If I ever get there, I believe I'll find you waiting for me!

Mrs. Dowey. With your tea ready!

Dowey. Ay, and good tea too!

Mrs. Dowey. (*Sitting as before*) Kenneth, we'll come back by Paris.

Dowey. (*Gaily*) I knew ye'd say that! All the leddies hankers to get to Paris!

Mrs. Dowey. (*Wistfully*) I want, before I die, to have a gown of Paris make, with dreamy corsage!

Dowey. We have a song about that. (*Half singing*)

> "Oh, Mistress Gill is very ill
> And nothing can improve her,
> But to see the Tuylleries
> And waddle through the Louvre."

(Both *laugh hilariously*.)

Mrs. Dowey. Kenneth, you must learn me that. (*Singing*)

> "Mistress Dowey's very ill
> And nothing can improve her—"

Dowey. (*Breaking in*)

> "But dressed up in a dreamy gown
> To waddle through the Louvre!"

(Both *laugh heartily again. Then he suddenly realizes she is getting round him.*) Now, now, now! What nonsense is this? (*He rises, going below the table and up left for his rifle.*) Well, thank you for my tea. I must be stepping.

Mrs. Dowey. (*Rising, goes left to his right*) Where are you living?

Dowey. (*Scratching his head*) That's the question. But there's a place called the Hut where some of the Fifth Battalion are. They'll take me in. (*Bitterly*) Beggars can't be choosers.

Mrs. Dowey. Beggars?

Dowey. I've never been here before. If you knew what it is to be in such a place without a friend! I was crazy with glee when I got my leave, at the thought of seeing London at last, but after wandering its streets for four hours I'd have been glad to be back in the trenches.

Mrs. Dowey. That's my position too, Kenneth. (*He nods.*) Twenty years have I been here. Folks is kind, but it's a foreign land to me.

Dowey. (*Kindly*) I'm sorry for you. (*Shouldering his kit*) But I see no way out for either of us. (*He turns away to pick up his rifle.*)

Mrs. Dowey. (*Longingly*) Do you not?

Dowey. (*Checking, turns to look at her*) Are you at it again?

Mrs. Dowey. Kenneth, I've heard that the thing a man on leave longs for more than anything is a bed with sheets and a bath.

Dowey. (*Grimly*) You never heard anything truer.

Mrs. Dowey. Go into that scullery, Kenneth. (*He looks at her sharply, then crosses right.*) And lift the table-top and tell me what you see. (*He gives her another look at the door, disappears for a moment and returns.*)

Dowey. It's a kind of bath.

Mrs. Dowey. You could do yourself pretty there half at a time.

Dowey. Me?

Mrs. Dowey. There's a woman through the wall that would be very willing to give me a shake-down till your leave's up.

Dowey. (*Snorting*) Oh, is there?

Mrs. Dowey. Kenneth—look!

(*Turning down left, she lets down the bed, then steps back for his approval.*)

Dowey. (*Striding over to left centre, examines this wonder*) Hullo! That's the dodge we need in the trenches.

Mrs. Dowey. That's your bed, Kenneth.

Dowey. (*Moved*) Mine! (*He grins queerly at her.*) You queer old body! You spunky little divert you! What can make you so keen to be burdened by a lump like me? (Mrs. Dowey *chuckles.*) I warn you I'm the commonest kind of man. I've been a kick-about all my life, and I'm no great shakes at the war.

Mrs. Dowey. (*Sitting on right end of the bed*) Yes, you are. How many Germans have you killed?

Dowey. (*To left end of the table*) Just two for certain, and there was no glory in it. It was just because they wanted my shirt.

Mrs. Dowey. Your shirt?

Dowey. Well, they said it was *their* shirt.

Mrs. Dowey. Have you took prisoners?

Dowey. I once took half a dozen, but that was a poor affair, too.

Mrs. Dowey. How could you take half a dozen?

Dowey. (*Hitching up his pack, casually*) Just in the usual way. I surrounded them.

Mrs. Dowey. (*Rising*) Kenneth, you're just my ideal.

Dowey. You're easy pleased. (*He crosses to the bed and feels it. Then, loosening his kit*) Old lady, if you really want me—I'll bide. (*He sets down his pack.*)

Mrs. Dowey. (*In a transport of joy*) Oh! Oh! Oh!

Dowey. But mind you, I don't accept you as a relation. (*Together they raise and replace the bed.*) For your personal glory you can go on *pretending* to the neighbours, but the best I can say for you is that you're on your probation. I'm a cautious character, and we must see how you turn out.

Mrs. Dowey. Yes, Kenneth.

Dowey. And now, I think, for that bath. (*He goes right towards the scullery and turns.*) My theatre begins at six-thirty. A cove I met on the bus is going with me.

Mrs. Dowey. (*Following him to centre*) You're sure you'll come back?

Dowey. I leave my kit in pledge.

Mrs. Dowey. You won't liquor up too freely, Kenneth?

Dowey. (*Coming a pace towards her, with a chuckle*) You're the first to care whether I did or not. (*He pats her arm.*) I promise. Tod! I'm beginning to look forward to being awakened in the morning by hearing you cry, "Get up, you lazy swine!" I've often envied men that had womenfolk with a right to say that. (*He goes right again to the scullery door, checks, and turns.*) By Sal and Tal!

Mrs. Dowey. (*A shade apprehensive*) What is it, Kenneth?

Dowey. (*Returning to right centre*) The theatre. It would be showier if I took a lady. (*He surveys her critically.*)

Mrs. Dowey. Kenneth, tell me this instant what you mean. Don't keep me on the jumps.

Dowey. (*Crosses down to her left—same business*) No, it couldn't be done.

Mrs. Dowey. Was it—*me* you were thinking of?

Dowey. (*Striding back to her right*) Ay, just for the moment. But you have no (*With a gesture*)—style.

Mrs. Dowey. (*Humbly*) Not in this, of course—but if you saw me in my merino! (*He is attentive.*) Kenneth, it's grand! It has a wee bit lace in the front!

Dowey. (*Drops down and sits on left end of the table*) Let's see it. (Mrs. Dowey *hurries to the chest of drawers and takes from the lower drawer the black merino, and brings it centre.*) Looks none so bad. (*He fingers it.*) Have you a bit of chiffon for the neck? (*She nods eagerly.*) It's not the Kaiser, nor bombs, nor keeping the home fires burning, nor Tipperary, that the men in the trenches think about. (*He shakes his head.*) It's—chiffon. (*Dubiously*) Any jewellery?

Mrs. Dowey. I have a brooch.

Dowey. Uh huh.

Mrs. Dowey. (*The boastful creature*) And I have a muff—and gloves.

Dowey. Ay, ay. (*Candidly*) Do you think you could give your face a less homely look?

Mrs. Dowey. I'm sure I could.

Dowey. Ay, ay. Then you can try. (*He goes up above the table and turns.*) But mind you, I promise nothing. It all depends—on the *effect*.

(*As he goes off into the scullery,* Mrs. Dowey *puts the dress on the chair left of the table.* Dowey *shuts the door, and the rush of the hot-water tap is heard.* Mrs. Dowey *goes right, takes up the letters and throws them contemp-*

*tuously into the fire.   She then rushes to the pail down
right, takes out the scrubbing-brush and swab, throwing
these on the floor.   She fills the pail from the kettle on the
hob, and brings it to left end of the table.   She is about to
wash, but checks.   She goes down left, takes a small mirror
from above the chest of drawers, and props it on the table
against the pail.   She examines her face and hair.   Licking
her palms, she smooths down her hair—)*

> The Curtain *falls for a few moments.*

SCENE TWO

(Five days later)

The Curtain *rises on the same scene, but the dishes are gone
from the table.   The gas is lit, the blinds are drawn.*

*There are chairs at each end of the table, and chairs above
and below the fireplace.* Dowey's *kit is up left against the
chair, his overcoat on the chair-back.   The bed is let down.
In the chest of drawers are—in the lower drawer her black
dress, and in the centre drawer her merino.   At this point, the
top drawer contains only the cash-box and Certificates, and a
small bag of lavender.*

Mrs. Mickleham *sits above the fire and* Mrs. Tully *is
below.   They are still in their charwoman clothes, but tidier.
Sleeves are pulled down, aprons clean, skirts are not tucked up,
and they wear hats.   A very lively conversation is in progress.*

Mrs. Mickleham. *(Speaking before the* Curtain *rises)*
I soon told him off. "Yes," I says, "you've got to make
your peace terms." *(The* Curtain *rises.)*   To which,
says he, "Then state your peace terms, ma'am," he
says. To which, I make reply, "Reparation, restitution,
and guarantys." (Mrs. Tully *nods with vigorous approval.*)
What do you think will happen, Sarah, after the war?
Will we go back to being as we were?

Mrs. Tully. If you mean us in the charring line— (*She rises, and kneeling, pokes the fire and brushes the grate.*)—speaking for myself, not *me*. The war has wakened me up, Amelia, to an understanding of my own importance that is truly astonishing.

Mrs. Mickleham. Same here. Instead of being the poor worms the likes of you and me thought we was, we turn out to be valiable parts of a great and 'aughty empire.

Mrs. Tully. (*Replaces poker, straightens up, and stands back to the fire*) When we have the vote, Amelia, will the men go on having it too?

Mrs. Mickleham. (*Graciously conceding*) At first. But after a bit— (Mrs. Haggerty *enters in bonnet and shawl. The other two exchange a disgusted glance. Privately*) Oh, here's that submarine again.

Mrs. Haggerty. Aren't they back, yet? (*She comes down to left of the table.*)

Mrs. Mickleham. No, we've been waiting this half-hour. They're at the theatre again.

Mrs. Haggerty. I just popped in with an insignificant present for him, as his leave's up. (*She moves above and to right end of the table.*)

Mrs. Tully. (*Stiffly*) The same errand brought us.

(Mrs. Haggerty *takes the chair from right of the table and draws it some little distance on* Mrs. Mickleham's *left.*)

Mrs. Haggerty. Though not in your set, Mrs. Mickleham, may I sit down? (*This is a timid attempt at a sneer.*)

Mrs. Mickleham. (*Distantly*) It's not our house.

(Mrs. Haggerty *sits. An awkward pause*)

Mrs. Haggerty. It's a terrible war.

(*Pause*)

Mrs. Tully. Is that so?

(*Pause*)

Mrs. Haggerty. (*Draws her chair a trifle nearer*) I wonder what will happen when it ends?

(*Pause*)

Mrs. Mickleham. I've no idea. (*She edges her chair nearer the fire, away from the intruder.*)

(Mrs. Tully *sits.*)

Mrs. Haggerty. (*After another pause*) My present is cigarettes.

Mrs. Mickleham. (*Annoyed*) So's mine.

Mrs. Tully. (*Ditto*) Mine too. (*Casually*) Mine has gold tips.

Mrs. Mickleham. (*Equally casual*) So has mine.

Mrs. Haggerty. (*Evidently without gold tips—whimpering*) What care I? Mine—is Exqui*ss*itos.

(*The* Others *titter.*)

Mrs. Mickleham. Excuse us, Mrs. Haggerty—if that's your name—but the word is Exqui*sy*tos.

Mrs. Haggerty. (*Stiffly*) Much obliged. (*She is inclined to weep.*)

Mrs. Mickleham. (*Rising*) I think I hear a taxi. (*She goes up to the window.*)

Mrs. Tully. (*Following her*) It'll be her third this week.

Mrs. Haggerty. (*As the* Others *peer out through the blind, she turns her chair.*) What is she in?

Mrs. Mickleham. A new astrakhan coat he gave her, with Venus sleeves.

Mrs. Haggerty. Has she sold her "Dainty Moments" coat?

Mrs. Mickleham. (*Coming down to above the table*) Not her. She has them both at the theatre. The one she's wearing, and the other she's carrying flung care-less-like over her arm.

(Mrs. Tully *comes down to the fireplace.*)

Mrs. Haggerty. (*To* Mrs. Mickleham) I saw her strutting with him yesterday as if the two of them made a procession. (Mrs. Mickleham *ignores this and returns to the window. To* Mrs. Tully) She was in her merino, of course.

(Mrs. Tully *turns away to the fireplace.*)

Mrs. Mickleham. Hsh! They're coming! (Mrs. Hag-gerty *rises, replaces the chair, and goes up to the window.*) She'll guess we're here as the light's on. Strike me dead if she's not come mincing in hooked on his arm! (*She crosses down to left of the table.*)

(*Enter* Mrs. Dowey *and* Dowey *as foretold; they leave the door open. Undoubtedly she is putting on airs. The astrakhan is over her merino, and she is in gloves, muff, and bonnet. A cloak is over her arm and she carries a small bag containing a champagne cork. It is not a comic get-up, but quiet and in good taste, though the effect is quaint. Dowey's clothes are now clean and his buttons, badges, etc., are bright.*)

Mrs. Dowey. Kenneth! We hae visitors!

Dowey. Your servant, ladies! (*He closes the door.*)

Mrs. Tully. Evening! We're not meaning to stay.

Mrs. Dowey. You're very welcome. (*Rather osten-tatiously*) Just wait till I get out of my muff (*She places it on the table with the bag.*)—and my astrakhan—and my cloak (*She places these on back of the chair left of the table.*)—and my Excelsior—(*This last is the bonnet, which she takes left to the chest of drawers.*)

Mrs. Mickleham. You've given her a glory time, Mr. Dowey.

Dowey. (*Throws his bonnet on the table, crossing to the fire, and warming his hands* It's her that has given it to me, ma'am.

(Mrs. Mickleham *moves above the table.*)

Mrs. Dowey. (*Returning to left of the table, giggling*) He! he! he! He just pampers me! The Lord forgive us, but being his last night, we had a sit-down supper at a restaurant! I swear, we had champagny wine! (*The* Others *are a little stiff.* Mrs. Dowey *takes the cork out of the bag and holds it up.*) And to them as doubts my words. There's the cork.

Mrs. Mickleham. (*Stiffly*) I'm sure.

Mrs. Tully. (*Approaching, and speaking across the table*) I would thank you, Mrs. Dowey, not to speak against my Alfred.

Mrs. Dowey. Me! (*She replaces the cork in her handbag.*)

Dowey. (*Crossing up between* Mrs. Tully *and* Mrs. Haggerty) Come, come, ladies! If you say another word I'll kiss the lot of you.

(*Pleased confusion;* Mrs. Tully *retires coyly down right.* Mrs. Haggerty *moves up centre, while* Mrs. Mickleham *comes left centre.*)

Mrs. Dowey. (*During the above*) Kenneth! (*Above the table*)

Mrs. Mickleham. Really! Them sodgers!

Mrs. Tully. The Kilties is the worst!

Mrs. Mickleham. I'm sure we don't grudge you your treats, Mrs. Dowey, and sorry we are that this is the end.

Dowey. Yes, it's the end. Leave's up. (*He glances at* Mrs. Dowey.) I must be off in ten minutes—

(Mrs. Dowey *makes a sudden bolt into the scullery. The* Others *turn and look sympathetically at the door.* Dowey *turns and goes to the fireplace, his face averted.*)

Mrs. Mickleham. Poor soul. (*They look at* Dowey.) We must run! (*She crosses to left end of the table, producing the cigarettes from her underskirt pocket.*) You'll be having some last words to say to her.

Dowey. (*Facing them with a worried expression*) I kept her out long on purpose, so as not to have much time to say them in.

Mrs. Tully. (*Putting her chair back against the wall down right*) It's the best way. (*She produces her cigarettes and goes up to* Dowey.) Just a mere nothing to wish you well, Mr. Dowey. (*She gives him the cigarettes, a little breathless, then goes up towards the door left centre.*)

Mrs. Mickleham. (*Crosses to him below the table, gives him cigarettes*) A scraping, as one might say. (*She turns and joins* Mrs. Tully, *below and on her left.*)

Mrs. Haggerty. (*Comes down right end of the table*) The heart is warm, though it may not be gold-tipped. (*She gives him the cigarettes, and retreats left to right of* Mrs. Tully.)

Dowey. (*Crossing quickly above and to left of the table, touched*) You bricks! (*He extends his hand.*) Shake! (*He shakes hands first with* Mrs. Haggerty, *then* Mrs. Tully, *lastly with* Mrs. Mickleham. *They retire to the* *door in that order*, Mrs. Haggerty *opening it. As he crosses left to the chair*) If you see a sodger man up there wi' this sort of thing (*Turning, indicates the kilt*), he's the one that's going back with me. (*He puts the cigarettes in his overcoat.*) Tell him not to come down, but to give me till the last moment, and then to whistle. (*He puts on his Tartan scarf.*)

Mrs. Tully.   I understand.   Good luck.

(*She exits to right.*)

Mrs. Mickleham.   Good luck!

(*She exits to right.*)

Mrs. Haggerty.   (*Pointing to his kilt*)   That's your style!

(*She exits to right,* Dowey *puts on his coat, buttons it up, closes the door up left, and stands. Then he tries to grin, but fails. Mutters, "Hell!" Then crosses determinedly to scullery door, and putting his head inside, calls:*)

Dowey.   Old lady!   (*He backs two paces left.*)

(Mrs. Dowey *comes out of the scullery. She is in her merino only, and once more a timid thing.*)

Mrs. Dowey.   Is it time?

Dowey.   Not yet.   I've left word with Dickson that he's to whistle when go I must.

Mrs. Dowey.   (*Crosses slowly and sits on the bed left*) All's ended.

Dowey.   (*Who is troubled himself; he crosses to left end of the table.*)   Now, now!   You promised to be gay.

Mrs. Dowey.   (*Looks up at him and tries to smile*)   Ay, Kenneth.

Dowey.   It's bad for me.   But it's worse for you.

Mrs. Dowey.   The men have their medals to win, you see.

Dowey. The women have their medals too. And they wear them in their hearts, where you wear yours. (*He sits on end of the table, and tries to be brusque.*) Come here! (*She starts to rise.*) No, I'll come to you. (*He crosses to right end of the bed, looking down at her.*) My God! You're a woman!

Mrs. Dowey. I had near forgot it.

Dowey. Have you noticed you have never called me "son"?

Mrs. Dowey. Have I noticed? I was feared, Kenneth. You said I was on probation.

Dowey. And so you were. Son! It's a little word, but you've made me value it. Well, the probation's ended.

Mrs. Dowey. Will I do?

Dowey. (*With a mischievous return to an earlier manner*) Woman, don't be so forward! Wait till I've proposed.

Mrs. Dowey. Propose for a mother?

Dowey. What for no? (*Kneeling*) Mrs. Dowey, have I your permission to ask you the most important question an orphan can ask of a nice old lady?

Mrs. Dowey. (*Giggling*) None of your sauce, Kenneth!

Dowey. For a long time, Mrs. Dowey, you cannot have been unaware of my sonnish feelings for you—

Mrs. Dowey. Wait till I get my mop to you!

Dowey. And if you're not willing to be my mother, I swear I'll never ask another—

(*She pulls his head down, embraces him, and strokes his hair. Her sadness has come back.*)

Mrs. Dowey. You're just trying to make me gay.

Dowey. I wish you could do the same for me. (*She smiles bravely.*) Was I a well-behaved infant, Mother?

Mrs. Dowey. Not you, sonny! You *were* a rampaging rogue!

Dowey. (*Sitting back on his heels*) Was I slow in learning to walk?

Mrs. Dowey. The quickest in our street! (*The chuckle dies on her lips. She rises.*) Was that—the whistle?

Dowey. No. no! (*He rises.*) See here, in taking me over you have, in a manner of speaking, joined the Black Watch. (*She puts her hands up to her eyes.*) So you've got to be as proud as—as that ghostly piper. (*He comes to attention.*) 'Shun! (*She obeys.*) That's the style! (*He goes to her.*) You've to be true to this little flag, you see. (*He indicates the little flag in her bodice.*)

Mrs. Dowey. I am true to it, Kenneth.

Dowey. You're great. (*He crosses up above the bed for the pack.*) I've sent your name in as being my nearest of kin. Your allowance will be coming to you weekly in the usual way.

Mrs. Dowey. Eh, is it wicked, Kenneth?

Dowey. (*Hitching on his pack*) I'll take the responsibility for it in both worlds. You see, I want you to be safeguarded in case anything hap—

Mrs. Dowey. Kenneth! (*Her head down, her hand out*)

Dowey. 'Shun! (*She obeys.*) Have no fear, I'll come back, covered with mud and medals. (*Trying to be brusque*) And mind you have that cup of tea waiting for me. Come here! (*He comes to below the bed. She approaches him, and he sits, pulling her down on his knee. She chuckles.*) What fun we'll have writing to each other. *Real* letters this time!

Mrs. Dowey. Ay!

Dowey. It would be a good plan if you began the first letter as soon as I've gone.

Mrs. Dowey. I will.

Dowey. I hope that Lady Dolly will go on sending me cakes.

Mrs. Dowey. You may be sure.

Dowey. (*Takes off his Tartan scarf and puts it round her neck*) You must have been a bonny thing when you were young.

Mrs. Dowey. (*Pushing him away playfully*) Away with you!

Dowey. It sets you fine.

Mrs. Dowey. Blue was always my colour.

(*The WHISTLE is heard. Mrs. Dowey rises, goes to the chair left of the table, her face averted. Dowey rises.*)

Dowey. 'Shun! (*She obeys. He goes to her, turns her round, and places his hands affectionately on her shoulders.*) Old lady, when I'm out there in the trenches, I'll have something to think of I never had before—home. This room, you with your mop and pail, are what Blighty means to me now.

(*She pulls his head down and kisses him on the forehead, then pulls herself together and runs into the scullery, closing the door. Dowey goes for bonnet and puts it on, and slings his rifle. An idea strikes him; he crosses quickly to right, takes pen, ink, and paper from the shelf above the fire and places them ready for Mrs. Dowey on the table.*

The WHISTLE is repeated. He glances at the window. Dowey goes to the scullery door, opens it, and peeps in.

We gather that Mrs. Dowey is on her knees, for he takes off his bonnet reverently, pauses, and then, turning away, goes out at the door up left centre as—)

The Curtain *falls.*

SCENE THREE

We have one last glimpse of the old lady—a month or two after Dowey's *death in action. When the* Curtain *rises, it is early morning. The blinds are up and the early sunshine streams in.*

On the table are certain articles, namely, Dowey's *bonnet, on the left of this a small packet of letters tied with ribbon, and the champagne cork. In the centre is the cash-box containing the Certificates.*

During this scene, low distant music of pipers playing the Black Watch Lament, "The Flowers of the Forest," is heard.

Mrs. Dowey *is kneeling at the chest of drawers, taking from a lower drawer her best dress. She rises with it, brushing it carefully with her hand, and takes it over to the table. She lays it down, brushes the bonnet, and places this on the dress. She then polishes the champagne cork with her apron and places it by the bonnet. The Lament ceases as she does this.*

Next, she opens the cash-box and examines the Certificates. Closing it, she places this, too, on the dress.

Faintly, the Lament re-commences. She takes up the letters, presses them for a moment to her bosom, and puts them on the dress. Then she lifts all, and crossing, takes them over to the drawer and lays them in.

She then takes the Tartan scarf from a top drawer and spreads it over the things in the lower one. Lastly, she takes a bag of lavender from the upper drawer and places this on the scarf, after smelling it. The Lament ceases.

Mrs. Dowey *closes the drawer gently. Then, turning to her pail and brushes down left, she picks them up, and goes slowly, bravely, off to her work through the door up left.*

SLOW CURTAIN

SOME DRAMATIC TERMS
and
NOTES AND QUESTIONS

THE STAGE

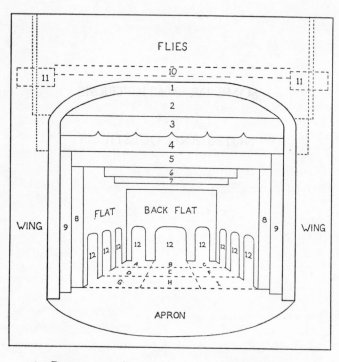

1. PROSCENIUM ARCH
2. FIRE CURTAIN
3. GRAND DRAPERY
4. FRONT CURTAIN
5. TEASER
6. BORDER
7. BORDER
8. RETURNS
9. TORMENTORS
10. BRIDGE
11. FLY GALLERY
12. ENTRANCES

A. *Up right*
B. *Up centre*
C. *Up left*
D. *Right centre*
E. *Centre*
F. *Left centre*
G. *Down right*
H. *Down centre*
I. *Down left*

SOME DRAMATIC TERMS

act—one of the principal divisions of a drama

adaptation—a play which is a modified version of the original piece of writing

amateur—one who acts for pleasure but not for money

antagonist—the opponent

apron—part of the deck in front of the proscenium arch

aside—a speech given by a character revealing his innermost thoughts while in the presence of others who pretend not to hear

blank verse—poetry written in unrhymed iambic pentameter

burlesque—a ludicrous play with overdrawn characters and situations

business—actions of the characters on stage

cast—the players

catastrophe—the last stage in the falling action of a tragedy, a tragic dénouement

catharsis—the emotional release the audience experiences through imaginative participation in a tragedy

centre—the centre of the stage

climax—the highest point of interest or emotion

comedy—a light drama which purposes amusement and ends happily

complication—the part of dramatic structure in which the entanglement of opposing forces is developed

conflict—the struggle which two opposing forces create

convention—a device or style that has been accepted because of its frequent use

costume play—a play in which actors appear in the style of historical dress to depict a period of time in the past

cue—the final words of an actor's speech indicating the time for another actor to speak or enter

curtain call—the calling of an actor before the curtain to receive the audience's applause due him after his performance

deck—floor of the stage

dénouement—the explanation or outcome of the plot's conflicts or intrigues

developing characters—characters who change during the development of the action

dialogue—words spoken by the actors

dimmer—equipment to decrease stage light

director—the person who guides the actors' interpretations of their rôles and is responsible for the overall effectiveness of the play

down stage—that section of the stage nearest the audience

drama—a serious play

dramatic irony—a device wherein the words or acts of a character have for the audience an added significance unintended and unperceived by the speaker

dress rehearsal—the final rehearsal of the play as it is actually to be presented

epilogue—the concluding statement of an actor after the close of the play proper

extravaganza—a fantastic, exaggerated dramatic composition

falling action—that part of dramatic structure in which the plot is unravelled

farce—a humorous play with gross incongruities and horseplay

flat—a piece of scenery composed of canvas stretched over a wooden frame

footlights—a row of floor lights at the front of the deck

gelatine—a transparent sheet available in different colours which can be placed over a spotlight to create effects

hero—the play's chief male character

heroine—the play's chief female character

house lights—the auditorium lights

ingénue—an actress who portrays an innocent young woman

lead—the principal part

left—the left side of the stage from the actor's point of view as he faces the audience

light-plot—the plan indicating the different lighting cues required at specific times

make-up—the paint, powder, and wigs which an actor puts on for a stage part

melodrama—a strongly emotional play with stock types, a conflict between good and evil, and poetic justice

motivation—the convincing cause for a character's action

movement—action

pageant—a medieval play performed on a stage on wheels, or a modern spectacle commemorating some historical event

pantomime—silent acting

pathos—that quality in a play that awakens feelings of sympathy and tender sorrow

plot—the planned actions of a play

preliminary exposition—information about events that have taken place before the opening of the play

professional—one who makes his living by acting

prologue—the introductory statement of an actor at the beginning of a play

prompter—one off stage who follows the actors' lines from the script and assists them if they forget

proscenium arch—the arch which holds the curtain

protagonist—the central figure in a play

realism—the presentation of life as it actually is

rehearsal—a private practice of a play before the public performance

right—the right side of the stage from the actor's point of view as he faces the audience

rising action—that part of dramatic structure in which the plot is complicated

royalty—a sum paid to the author for permitting the use of his play

scene—one of the minor divisions of a drama, usually a subdivision of an act

scenery—painted flats, screens, and hangings used to create a certain effect, realistic or impressionistic, as a background for the play's action

script—the manuscript

sketch—a brief dramatic performance

soliloquy—a speech given by a character revealing his innermost thoughts while he is alone on stage

spotlight—a bright, concentrated light directed upon an actor or object to gain prominence

stock characters—conventional types, for example, the villain, the hero, the prince charming

structure—the planned framework or arrangement of parts of a play

subplot—a subordinate plot which may be directly related to the main plot or almost unessential to it

tormentor—a wing or curtain on each side of the stage, behind the front curtain

tragedy—a play with a calamitous ending

tragic irony—dramatic irony in a tragedy

understudy—one who learns the rôle of another in a play for the purpose of substituting if necessary

unities—three principles of dramatic structure—time, place, and action (detailed account on page 208)

up stage—that section of the stage farthest from the audience

wings—the sides of the stage outside the deck where the acting takes place

NOTES AND QUESTIONS

The Monkey's Paw

WILLIAM WYMARK JACOBS (1863-1943) was born in London, England. After his education at private schools, he was appointed to the Savings Bank Department of the General Post Office as a clerk. In 1896 his first book *Many Cargoes* was published, and in 1899 he resigned his Civil Service post to devote more time to creative writing. Although he is known primarily as a humorist because of his many witty articles, he has also achieved fame in the short story field because of his popular tales of horror. One of these, *The Monkey's Paw*, is considered a classic of its genre. Here, as he skilfully reveals the terror of the unknown, one sees the tinge of pessimism that many critics feel is part of Jacobs. In collaboration with Louis N. Parker this story was dramatized and a number of plays, mostly one-act comedies, were written. Best known of his plays are *Establishing Relations*, *The Warming Pan*, *A Distant Relative*, and *Dixon's Return*. His last published book, which appeared in 1931, was a collection of previously published stories. A few days before his eightieth birthday, Jacobs died in a London nursing home.

LOUIS NAPOLEON PARKER (1852-1944) was born in France, of English-speaking parents. During his early years, he lived on the continent, but when he was still a boy, the family returned to England. There he attended the Royal Academy of Music. He first devoted his talents to teaching and writing music. About the year 1890, however, he began to write and adapt plays and became known as an excellent craftsman of the theatre. Before his death in 1944, he had applied his dramatic skill to more than one hundred plays, the most famous of which is *Disraeli* (1911).

SUGGESTIONS FOR PRODUCING THE PLAY

This supernatural story begins with a happy domestic scene in the White's living-room and ends there with a climax so compelling and nearly tragic that the audience reaches a pinnacle of tension seldom experienced in the theatre today. We are asked to believe the superstition that the possessor of a certain monkey's paw is granted three wishes by asking them aloud. Although our reason may reject the idea as ridiculous, so well written is the play that our imagination accepts the possibility.

To create the eerie atmosphere suitable for such a horror play, the dramatist requires special effects: the howling of wind, a gruesome monkey's paw, a flickering candle, a loud, unnatural knocking, and moonlight. Unless this play is carefully rehearsed, the results can be disastrous.

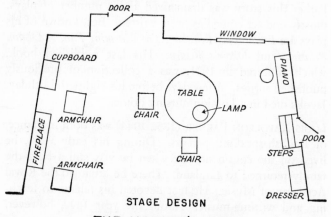

STAGE DESIGN

THE MONKEY'S PAW

Many amateur performances have suffered from poor synchronization of a wind machine or wind recording with the opening of the door. Laughter, too, has unintentionally been created by the candle's not being blown out at the exact moment required, the bolt's not sticking as it should, and a rapping so loud that the actors' speeches are completely drowned by the noise from outside. On the other hand, if the play is well presented, few one-act plays have so powerful an effect on the audience.

Follow the detailed stage direction carefully. The stage business is explained and the actors themselves are described. Such hints will help greatly in the casting problem. Remember, Mr. and Mrs. White are ordinary, old people whose greatest joy is their son. It is the vivid contrast of this normal, simple picture with the supernatural horror of what is happening to them that gives the play impact. Mrs. White, then, may wear a simple housedress; Mr. White, a grey coat sweater and grey trousers. To age these characters, #20 white greasepaint and white powder may be applied to their hair.

For several rehearsals before the final performance, Morris should practise having his arm tied to his side or behind him, to indicate that he has only one arm; otherwise, he will be unable to work smoothly with the properties. Be careful with this play, and you will have your audience talking about its success for months.

NOTES

Fulham (foŏ'lum)—a metropolitan borough of London, England

Chitral—the capital of Chitral state, where in 1895 a small British force was besieged and relieved in a memorable fashion. In 1947 Chitral state acceded to Pakistan. Remember, *The Monkey's Paw* was first produced in 1903.

grog—Grog is a mixture of any spirits, especially rum and water. Admiral Vernon, or Old Grog as his sailors called him, is credited with being the first to dilute the rum on board ship. The nickname comes from the grogram cloak he wore on deck in bad weather.

a cove—an individual. The word is from old thieves' slang.

shirty—bad-tempered. This is the state you are in when someone has "got your shirt out."

fakir—Loosely, the term applies to Moslem or Hindu holy men noted for their asceticism and indifference to pain. More accurately, a fakir is a Mohammedan religious beggar who wears dark, coarse clothes and performs menial tasks. Often these men are called "wonder workers."

Arabian nights—This is a series of fanciful stories in Arabic told by Scheherazade to her cruel husband the Sultan Schahriah over a period of one thousand and one nights. By thus amusing him, she caused him to revoke his decree that he would have a new wife every night and have her strangled at daybreak. The stories of Ali Baba and Aladdin are part of this collection, which first appeared in its present form about 1450 in Cairo.

specs—This is a colloquial abbreviation of the word *spectacles*.

Questions

A

Scene 1

1. Notice that the playwright gives a detailed description of the White's living-room. Select the word from that passage which best conveys the impression he is trying to create.
2. Find a line that indicates that Mrs. White knows her husband's character very well.
3. State the different reactions of the characters to the first appearance of the monkey's paw.

4. What is special about the monkey's paw?

Scene 2

5. Select the references which suggest that Mrs. White has been thinking of the paw.

6. How does Mrs. White's conduct in this scene contribute to reader tension?

7. Outline Sampson's interview with the Whites.

Scene 3

8. What thought suddenly occurs to Jenny?

9. Comment on White's objection to wishing again.

General

10. Imagine that you are a wealthy Hollywood producer who plans to make a motion picture of *The Monkey's Paw*. After a consideration of the physical stature, voice, manner, appearance, and acting ability required, choose famous personalities who seem most suitable for the rôles.

B

Scene 1

1. Why is Mr. White angry?

2. Give reasons for saying that knocking is an effective stage device.

3. How does the storm contribute to the dramatic impact of the scene?

4. Account for Herbert's scepticism of Morris' stories.

5. Justify Morris' giving the correct method of wishing although he evidently wanted White to pitch the paw on the fire again.

6. Find some evidence of Mrs. White's thrift.

Scene 2

7. What do you consider the most pathetic touch in this scene?

8. Why is the final line very effective?

Scene 3

9. If you were directing this scene, what differences of voice, action, and lighting would you stress in contrast with Scene 1?

General

10. In writing a character sketch of Mr. White, illustrate each trait mentioned with a detailed reference. The good character sketch suggests some of the mental, physical, and spiritual qualities of a person and exemplifies or explains these characteristics in a clear, interesting manner.

C

Scene 1

1. Prove that Herbert is very important to his parents' happiness.
2. Give reasons for the dramatist's presenting the sergeant as physically handicapped.
3. Read aloud Herbert's speech wherein he refuses a drink. In what way is the passage ironic?
4. From the following list select the words which best characterize the sergeant-major: garrulous, imaginative, eccentric, boastful, flattering, hypocritical, irritable, and domineering. Give reasons for your choice.
5. Explain why the author does not have Morris tell us what his three wishes were.
6. Discuss how the dramatic crisis of Mr. White's first wish is made effective on stage.
7. Near the end of the scene, White says, "This bolt's stiff again! I must get Herbert to look to it in the morning." Why did the playwright stress this in Scene 1?

Scene 2

8. What aspects of this scene are in contrast to Scene 1?

Scene 3

9. The last scene increases in tension to almost unbearable heights. Besides the loud knocking, what other factors contribute to this atmosphere of suspense?

General

10. In preparing a plot graph of *The Monkey's Paw*, include at least ten significant points of action. Mark off the structural divisions of introduction, rising action, climax, and conclusion.

The Happy Journey

THORNTON WILDER (1897-   ) was born in Madison, Wisconsin and educated in China and the United States of America. After his graduation from Yale in 1920, he accepted a teaching position at the Lawrenceville School in New Jersey and later, at the University of Chicago. His first novel, *The Cabala*, a story of sophisticates in Rome, appeared in 1925 and received the critics' acclaim. It was not, however, till 1927 and *The Bridge of San Luis Rey*, another novel, that he was hailed internationally. Besides the Pulitzer Prize won for this effort, he received another in 1938 for his magnificent *Our Town*, a study in play form of small-town New England life. Still a third Pulitzer Prize was awarded him for *The Skin of Our Teeth*—a dramatically unconventional synopsis of man's efforts to preserve civilization throughout history. From 1935 on, he devoted his creative talent almost exclusively to the stage. Some of his noted dramatic works are *The Happy Journey*, *The Angel that Troubled the Waters* (a collection of three-minute plays), *The Long Christmas Dinner* (a one-act play collection), and *Merchant of Yonkers*. Although he stands for the unconventional in drama, few playwrights living today possess his great power to move an audience through laughter and tears. All his creative efforts stress individualism of form and approach. While his subject matter encompasses the mystery of death, the pity of life, and the tragedy of beauty, he strongly emphasizes the essential dignity of man.

SUGGESTIONS FOR PRODUCING THE PLAY

This is the simple story of a mother, father, and their two children who travel from Newark to Camden to visit Beulah, the married daughter. Such simplicity is emphasized by Wilder's presentation: no scenery is required, and four chairs and a cot are the only properties used. The four chairs, placed on a low platform, represent the family automobile, and it is wise to raise the two rear chairs to improve the audience's view of the children who sit there. It is the dramatist's purpose here to stimulate the imagination, and therefore any use of imaginary properties must be carried out with detailed pantomime, for example, Arthur's marble playing, entering the car, and eating the hot dogs.

There is more, however, to the play than a simple story simply told. Wilder's portrayal is a refreshing contrast to traditional drama. Think of the Stage Manager's rôle. He

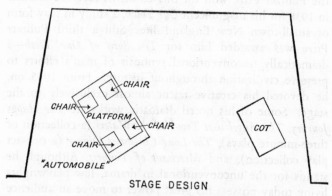

STAGE DESIGN

THE HAPPY JOURNEY

is expected to place and remove "the automobile," read directly from his script, play several parts, and even eat an apple, smoke, or read a newspaper, while the play is in progress! Such unconventional behaviour so delighted audiences, that many modern dramatists have since copied Wilder's innovations.

Although the comic atmosphere is present in *The Happy Journey*, do not forget that the play's main purpose is the presentation of Ma's character. Wilder is primarily interested in the dignity of the human soul, and there is a strength and greatness in Ma that can be very beautiful and moving.

As far as costumes are concerned, contemporary dress will do. Stress, however, a slight primness in the clothes that Caroline and Ma wear. Even Pa may appear a bit old-fashioned.

Beware of two extremes of presentation—false sentimentality and exaggerated acting. The characters are not caricatures: they are flesh and blood people with whom the audience must find an easy identification.

Notes

Newark—the largest city in New Jersey, a state in eastern United States of America

Camden—a main city in western New Jersey. Camden is on the Delaware River.

Elizabeth branch—the chapter of the lodge in Elizabeth, New Jersey

peakèd—a colloquial expression meaning thin or wan

speak-easies—a slang term that denotes unlicensed drinking places where liquor may be obtained illegally

Y.M.C.A.—Young Men's Christian Association

Knights of Columbus—This Roman Catholic society for men was founded in 1882 at New Haven, Connecticut to unite laymen of the church in religious and civic usefulness.

Trenton—the capital of New Jersey. On December 20,

1776, Washington crossed the Delaware River in a surprise attack and captured about 900 Hessians, mercenary soldiers employed by Great Britain against the colonies in the American Revolution.

QUESTIONS

A

1. From the beginning of the play, select lines that show Ma's anxiety.
2. To what extent is Arthur a typical teen-age boy?
3. What is the purpose of the Kirbys' journey to Camden?
4. Why is Arthur afraid of going by the school?
5. How does Arthur outrage Ma?
6. Outline the scene between the two of them when she forgives him.
7. Read aloud the speech where Caroline tries to impress her mother and father with her intelligence. Why does she do so?
8. Suggest words to describe the feeling of the family as they sing together.
9. Wilder does not describe the physical appearance of his characters. Instead, he lets their words and actions create their images. Describe your picture of Beulah.

General

10. Give five reasons for the continued popularity of this play.

B

1. Define pantomime.
2. From the unit of action that takes place in the Kirby home, name several features that would command audience attention.
3. Examine Ma's speeches carefully. How do they help give you a mental image of the woman?
4. Find references that show her sympathetic attitude, religious nature, sense of humour, and strength.

5. Why do the children get embarrassed by their mother's conduct?

6. Have three volunteers read aloud Ma's speech about people being rich. Vote to determine who has best interpreted the speech. Give reasons for your choice.

7. The scene between Ma and Beulah is very intimate. If you were in charge of lighting, how would you intensify the dramatic quality of this scene?

8. Select examples of pathos from the conversation between Ma and Beulah.

9. How does Ma dominate that scene?

General

10. To be effective, pantomimes utilize silent motion, gesture, and facial expression. Select three pantomimes from the play, and enact them in class. Discuss how successful each is. Some suggested pantomimes are the Kirbys' leaving their house, entering the car, Arthur and the hot dogs, and identifying the landmarks.

C

1. Why does Wilder have his characters use imaginary properties such as the marbles, mirror, window, and hot dogs, instead of real ones?

2. The author had considered *The Portrait of a Lady* as the title for this play. In what ways is *The Happy Journey* a better choice?

3. Discuss why Wilder had the Stage Manager play so many different parts rather than introduce new characters.

4. Notice the stress on the sudden jolts and lurches of the people in the car. If you were directing this play, how would you create the impression that the characters are passengers in an actual automobile which is starting and stopping, rather than four people sitting on four chairs?

5. Give three dramatic gains of having the children read aloud signboards during the journey.

6. The playwright intersperses comic and serious moments in this work. Consider the effect on the audience of the funeral unit of action coming when it does in the play.

7. Some critics suggest that the children seem too young for teen-agers: Arthur is supposed to be thirteen and Caroline, fifteen. Justify Wilder's references to marbles and wishing on stars as part of their behaviour pattern.

8. It seems unusual for Pa and Arthur to leave almost immediately instead of going into Beulah's house for a few minutes. Why did Wilder get them off stage?

9. What does the singing at the end of the play contribute?

General

10. Good dialogue is vital to the success of any play. Not only should the conversations advance plot and reveal character, but also they should seem natural and consistent with the speakers' natures. Playwrights often vary the length, rhythm, and language of speeches to contrast characters; notice how short Elmer's speeches are compared to Ma's.

   For class dramatization, write a planned dialogue for the Kirbys. Depict some event that takes place during their return journey home. Your passage should contain at least fifty different speeches.

The Patchwork Quilt

RACHEL LYMAN FIELD (1894-1942), born in New York City, spent most of her early life in New England. Her first success in the field of letters was a one-act play called *Three Pills in a Bottle*, which she wrote while a student at Radcliffe College in Massachusetts. After college, Miss

Field continued to write, and within a few years, she began a career as an author of children's books. In 1929 she published *Hitty*, which was awarded the Newberry Medal as the finest piece of children's literature for that year. From 1930 on, Miss Field began to write more for adults, and in 1938 came her most popular book, *All This and Heaven Too*. People who knew Rachel Field said that she was a friendly, modest person whom success did not change. She lived quietly with her husband Arthur Pederson and daughter Hannah until her death in 1942.

Suggestions for Producing the Play

This play's power lies in the strong and immediate sympathy of the audience for old, bewildered Mrs. Willis. Confronting her are the cold, practical Wendalls, who want possession of her deed to some valuable property. Such a situation is dramatically explosive. To complicate matters, we learn that Mrs. Willis' mind wanders, and we fear that she might unwittingly reveal the hiding place of the document to her conniving daughter and son-in-law, who are very willing to declare her legally incompetent. The only source of strength for the feeble widow is her granddaughter Betty. Although the ending is pathetic, the audience feels relieved that the Wendalls' selfish scheme failed.

The heavy pathos of this play is relieved by two flash-backs that show the tenderness and sensitivity of the writer. These same flash-backs can be the most effective units in the entire play if they are carefully produced. There should be an aura of other-worldliness about their presentation. The distinction between them and the real situation of old Mrs. Willis must be crystal clear. One important aid in producing this required effect is proper lighting: we are told that firelight falling on the figures that step from the shadows makes them visible to the audience. Do not use a red filter to secure this effect; instead, combine an orange and light rose filter. This illumination and the characters' clothes "in the style of fifty years ago" contribute much to the desired atmosphere. Remember, though, that the people in the flash-back must be completely unaware of Mrs. Willis' cries and gestures: they must be absorbed in each other. Once their unit of action is finished, they merely step back into the shadows and off stage.

Two other lighting suggestions deserve mention. After the flash-backs, the electric lights are turned full on: Mrs. Willis is dazzled by their brightness. Hard reality is strikingly present. Then, after the resigned Joe and Anne leave, the lights are gradually dimmed while the pathetic old lady moves slowly about her room.

Special care must also be taken in casting this play. The characters of Emily and Betty may be played by the same child. Two different actresses, if they resemble each other closely, may play Molly at twenty and at twenty-seven.

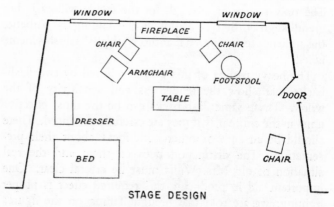

STAGE DESIGN

THE PATCHWORK QUILT

More effective, however, although it necessitates a quick costume change, is to have the same actress play Molly in the two flash-backs and thus give an authentic portrayal.

This play represents the best of Rachel Field's work. The gentle tenderness and the compelling pathos that she so beautifully creates are present here. She is an artist who primarily makes us feel rather than think. If *The Patchwork Quilt* is competently handled, it is a memorable theatrical experience.

NOTES

pastel—a picture drawn with pastels, crayons made by mixing gum-water and ground paints

tatting—a lace-edging made with a hand shuttle by looping and knotting thread

a satin that can stand alone—Molly here praises the richness and heaviness of the material that enable it to keep its shape in folds without the benefit of crinolines.

making me a call—visiting me

puff—a quilted bed-covering

QUESTIONS

A

1. Why is this play called a fantasy?
2. Suggest another suitable title.
3. In what state of mind is Mrs. Willis as the curtain opens?
4. Outline the Wendalls' plan.
5. Explain why the old quilt is so important to Mrs. Willis.
6. Narrate what happened in the first flash-back.
7. What was William's present to Molly?
8. Tell the secret of the white patch.
9. How is the spell of the second flash-back broken?

General

10. Write brief notes on the dramatic contribution of each of the following:

    (*a*) Emily

    (*b*) Mr. Jenkins

    (*c*) white lilacs

    (*d*) Katy's room

    (*e*) "It's all grey now."

B

1. Select three references that emphasize Mrs. Willis' distracted mental state.

2. Suggest apt words to describe Anne's character.

3. The old lady seems no match for the calculating Wendalls. What support, though, does she get to ensure the audience that the conflict is not over-balanced?

4. Which of Joe's lines seems most despicable?

5. Summarize the essential details of the second flash-back.

6. Describe the effect that it has on Mrs. Willis.

7. Why did the characters in the flash-backs ignore Mrs. Willis' responses?

8. Discuss how effective it is to let the audience know the secret for which the characters are searching.

9. Find the most pathetic touch in the play.

General

10. One very important staging device is the use of contrast: people with striking mental, moral, and physical *differences* are brought together to sharpen the conflict.

    Find at least five distinct contrasts of character in *The Patchwork Quilt*.

C

1. In the opening description of the set, the writer states, "the only picture which seems to be a personal belonging is a portrait in an oval gold frame over the fireplace." If you were a set designer, how would you suggest to the audience that this picture alone "seems to be a personal belonging"?
2. Why is the subject of the patchwork quilt introduced early in the play?
3. The fact that the town-hall at Green River burned down seems contrived. Explain why it is necessary for the plot to have such a coincidence.
4. Account for the audience's accepting the flash-back of Molly's wedding day, instead of objecting to it on the grounds that it ruins the realism of the play?
5. Notice that Molly had a premonition of the future. Give reasons why dramatists are fond of this device.
6. Name four points of contrast between Molly's past life and her present existence.
7. Suggest two reasons why the authoress did not include Anne in a flash-back.
8. Towards the end of the play, tension mounts higher and higher. Read aloud three speeches that contribute greatly to suspense.
9. Although the ending is not happy, the audience feels satisfied. Why?

General

10. A television director of a dramatic show must plan his action according to the type of image or "shot" he wants to appear on the screen at a given instant. Three basic "shots" predominate: the long shot, the close-up, and the medium shot. As the name suggests, the long shot shows as much of the subject as possible, to help establish an overall impression. For example, a

director might use a long shot including a dark stormy night, an eerie castle, and a lone traveller, to create a mood of mystery. The close-up, on the other hand, lets people see clearly what is taking place. It establishes an intimacy between the viewer and actor, and enables the director to emphasize special objects or facial expressions. Finally, the medium shot refers to any intermediary stage between the long shot and the close-up.

Imagine that you are to direct this play as a television presentation. Write clear, detailed instructions to the cameraman explaining what basic "shots" you require for the second flash-back. Make certain that you identify the "shot" with definite speeches. For example,

Emily. Why—it crackles. (*close-up of white patch*)

After three volunteers have explained their camera plans vote to determine whose instructions would create the best dramatic effects.

The Valiant

HOLWORTHY HALL (1887-1936), in reality H. E. Porter, was born in Boston. After his graduation *cum laude* from Harvard University in 1907, he took the name of a dormitory—Holworthy Hall—as his pseudonym. He served as President of A. D. Porter Company, publishers, from 1915 to 1916. Although his light fiction was well received in large national magazines, it was not until *The Valiant*, a one-act melodrama written with his classmate Robert Middlemass, an actor, that he achieved considerable fame. His literary efforts were varied—novels, plays, and short stories. Some of his principal efforts are *My Next Imitation* (1913), *Pepper* (1915), *Paprika* (1916), *What He Least Expected* (1917), *The Six Best Cellars* (with H. McNair

Kahler in 1919), *The Man Nobody Knew* (1919), *Aerial Observation* (1921), *The Valiant* (1924), and *Colossus* (1930). He died in 1936 of pneumonia at Charlotte Hungerford Hospital, Torrington, Connecticut.

ROBERT MIDDLEMASS (1886-1949), best known as an actor, was also a dramatist and a director. He was born in New Britain, Connecticut, and completed his schooling with graduation from Harvard in 1909. Since that date until his death in 1949, he was actively connected with the theatre.

Besides writing revue and vaudeville sketches, Mr. Middlemass was the author of the one-act plays, *Our Dearest Possession*, *Search Me*, *The Under Dog*, and the three-act play, *The Budget*. He also co-authored three long plays, *The Handy Man*, *Americans All*, and *The Clutching Claw*, directed their productions, and acted in two of them. His career as an actor included appearances in fifteen Broadway successes.

SUGGESTIONS FOR PRODUCING THE PLAY

The Valiant, a frequent winner in amateur play competitions, is one of the most popular one-act plays ever written. Its effect on an audience can be impressive because of the strange situation and appealing characterization presented. The authors confront us with a puzzle that is fascinating: a condemned murderer refuses to divulge his identity or his motive for the crime. The suspense thus engendered, in combination with the pathos of the interview between the tender, trusting Josephine and the hardened, unrelenting criminal Dyke, creates a powerful dramatic experience.

There is, however, a danger inherent in the play. Unless the characters are "underplayed," the melodrama breaks loose and a farce results. The Warden's anxiety and concern should not be hammered home. Nor should Father Daly be a stock spiritual shadow. Beware of over-emphasizing Dyke's callousness at first, or his later tenderness will seem inconsistent. Then too, although Josephine is naïve, she is not stupid. It is her trusting nature, not her gullibility, that must show through. Remember, these are real human beings with strengths and weaknesses, and although they are caught up in a somewhat artificial situation, they must not strain our credulity.

Fortunately, the authors have clearly described the characters and the set in detail. You would be wise to consider carefully their suggestions for your presentation. Only one textual note may create some confusion: the description of Josephine Paris. We are told that she is "fresh and wholesome, and rather pretty; but her manner betrays a certain spiritual aloofness from the ultra-modern world—a certain delicate reticence of the flesh—which immediately separates her from the metropolitan class. Indeed she is dressed far too simply for a metropolitan girl of her age; ... she is self-unconscious. She looks at the Warden squarely, but not in boldness, and yet not in feminine appeal; she has rather the fearlessness of a girl

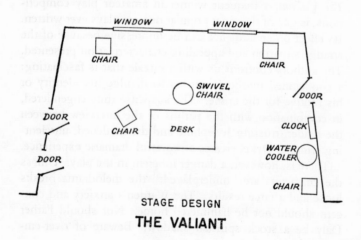

STAGE DESIGN

THE VALIANT

who has lost none of her illusions about men in general. Her expression is essentially serious; it conveys, however, the idea that her seriousness is due to her present mission, and that ordinarily she takes an active joy in the mere pleasure of existence." This is a complex character for any actress to comprehend, let alone portray! It is better to play her simply as a trusting, naïve, rather serious girl, who has journeyed a long way to try to discover whether Dyke is the brother she has not seen in eight years.

Two final points have particular application to this play. The first is that just as important as acting is reacting: the gestures. facial expressions, emotional responses, and pantomime are often as telling as dialogue well delivered. Equally important is the correct pacing of a drama. Generally, the cues should be picked up quickly in order to achieve spontaneity and realism, but on certain occasions, a slow pace is essential. The ending of this play is most effective if there are moments of purposeful silence, for example, the jailer's final entrance, Father Daly's and the Warden's knowing glances at each other, Dyke's sudden realization that the time of execution has come, and his slow, pitiable gaze at Father Daly and the Warden. If the play is well done, it is a delight to act in, and an intense pleasure to view.

NOTES

oscillation—a wavering

to get in awful Dutch with me—"In Dutch" once meant "in prison"; here, the expression "to get in Dutch" means "to get in wrong." In colloquial English use, "Dutch" often has a derisive or belittling application and dates back to the rivalry between England and Holland in the seventeenth century.

peremptorily—authoritatively

spread-eagle district attorney—Spread-eagle oratory is a combination of exaggeration, bombast, effrontery, figurative language, platitudes, and threats. Dyke here refers to the boastful, exaggerating, bombastic speech of the man who brought him to trial.

insouciant—unconcerned

"Thou knowest the mask of night is on my face..."
(*Romeo and Juliet*, Shakespeare, Act 2, Scene 2)

vacuity—lack of intelligence

"Good-night, good-night, parting is such sweet sorrow..." (*Romeo and Juliet*, Shakespeare, Act 2, Scene 2)

The Jerries—This was the army nickname in World War I for the Germans.

box barrage—In this military tactic a curtain of bursting shells is fired to fall in front of advancing troops and to act as a protective covering for them.

howitzers—These are short cannons that hurl shells at a higher angle of elevation than ordinary cannon.

a few heavies—heavy artillery

"Sleep dwell upon thine eyes, peace in thy breast..."
(*Romeo and Juliet*, Shakespeare, Act 2, Scene 2)

"Of all the wonders that I yet have heard..."
(*Julius Caesar*, Shakespeare, Act 2, Scene 2)

"Cowards die many times before their death..."
(*Julius Caesar*, Shakespeare, Act 2, Scene 2)

"I will lift up mine eyes unto the hills..."
(*The Bible*, Psalm 121)

QUESTIONS

A

1. Describe the setting of the play.
2. How is suspense aroused at the opening of the scene?
3. Why is the Warden in a disturbed state of mind?
4. Explain the contribution to story interest of the Governor's call.

5. Summarize the Warden's appeal to Dyke regarding the letters.
6. Outline the interview between the girl and the Warden.
7. How does she hope to identify her brother?
8. Relate her attempts to recognize him.
9. In your recounting of the story that Dyke tells about Josephine's brother, stress the details which convince the girl of its truth.

General

10. Draw an original, detailed diagram of the stage set as described on page 77. Include properties, doors, and actors' positions for the opening curtain.

B

1. Why do the authors give a detailed description of the Warden?
2. Select the lines which summarize his philosophy of life.
3. Show that the conversation between Warden Holt and Father Daly is a good way to introduce James Dyke.
4. How did the Warden acquire the Liberty Bonds?
5. Some people suggest that the Governor's call is far-fetched and therefore a flaw. What is your opinion?
6. Account for Dyke's apparent lack of appreciation of the Warden's letting him stay in his office rather than go back to the cell.
7. Why do the authors stress the girl's youth and innocence?
8. Find the clues that the dramatists give to suggest that Dyke is inventing the story of Joseph Anthony Paris.
9. What elements of the ending are highly dramatic?

General

10. Various methods of characterization are used by dramatists: (*a*) a person's speeches, (*b*) his acts, (*c*) his gestures, (*d*) his facial expressions, (*e*) his

clothes, and (*f*) what others say about him. Find one example of each method from this play and state the characteristic revealed.

C

1. Preliminary exposition, a term applied to facts or events of the plot supposed to have taken place before the action of the play proper, is often vital to the understanding of the play. Find five examples of preliminary exposition and discuss how skilfully they have been introduced.

2. Although Dyke wanted anonymity, he eagerly desired to write his autobiography. Explain the apparent contradiction.

3. Discuss how convincingly the dramatists avoided the technical difficulty of producing the interview with Dyke in his small jail cell as would seem natural.

4. Why did the authors include the dialogue passage between the Warden and the Jailer?

5. Compare Dyke's views of the soul and the hereafter with your own.

6. Why must Joe's interest in stories and books be stressed?

7. How do you know that James Dyke is really Joseph Anthony Paris?

8. What questions are still left unanswered at the end of the play?

9. Explain the significance of the title.

General

10. The unities are principles of dramatic structure involving time, place, and action. The unity of time developed from Aristotle's statement that "Tragedy endeavours as far as possible to confine itself to a single revolution of the sun, or but slightly to exceed this limit." Many later dramatists followed the twenty-four hour limit,

while some insisted upon an exact correspondence between the actual amount of play time on stage and the action of the play. Another unity, the unity of place, confines the action to one setting. Perhaps the most important and effective is the unity of action, which demands that the action be complete; that is, it should have a beginning, middle, and ending. Realize, however, that some great dramatists have disregarded these principles with some success. The playwrights who obey them feel that they gain considerable power and impact from the concentration that the unities afford.

Write a clear, interesting account of what use the authors of this play have made of the unities.

Moon-Up

ROBERT ARTHUR was born shortly before World War I, on the island of Corregidor, in the Philippines. As a contributor to his high school paper, he began his literary career; soon after, he made his first sale to an adventure magazine at the age of 17. Since his graduation from the University of Michigan's Department of Journalism, he has lived in many parts of the United States, always as a writer or editor. He has written several hundred short stories of mystery and science-fiction, as well as a great many radio dramas. He has also written some television plays, but *Moon-Up* is his only published play. It was inspired by the sight of an abandoned house perched high on the edge of a river bank in Kentucky.

SUGGESTIONS FOR PRODUCING THE PLAY

Robert Arthur in *Moon-Up* presents us with an electrifying conflict. The kindly Tom, older son of the feeble Ma Holloway, has tried to keep from his mother the information that her favourite son, Harry, is a criminal. It soon becomes clear that the latter, having escaped from jail, is making his way to the isolated Holloway home in the Kentucky hills. When he arrives, he threatens to reveal his past to his mother, and Tom is torn between his duty to help the Sheriff capture this murderer and his desire to save Ma from the fatal shock of learning the truth about her son. After Tom solves his problem, the reader is astounded, yet satisfied, by the shocking climax.

What saves the play from melodrama is the credibility of the characterization. In casting, pay attention to the detailed physical descriptions of the characters. Be careful, too, to show that Ma, although an old woman confined to a wheel chair, still possesses a strong will. Contrast carefully your presentations of Tom and Harry. Tom is between thirty and forty, while Harry is in his late twenties. Stress Tom's slowness and kindness and Harry's swiftness and viciousness. Tom is a countryman; Harry belongs to the city. Contrast, too, the sheriff, whose aggressiveness

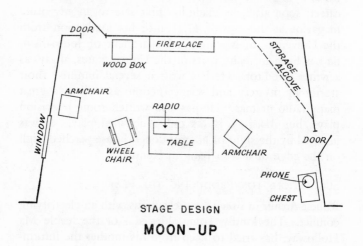

STAGE DESIGN

MOON-UP

and boldness keep the story moving at a fast pace, with Tom, who is quietly perplexed by his conflict.

Since this is a drama of suspense, the tension must build and build till the final curtain. In the opening interview with Ma, Tom's kindliness should be pre-eminent, but there should be a trace of anxiety in his words and movements. The audience should, moreover, feel the power and urgency of the river as it roars by the house surrounded by darkness. With Ma's premonition of Harry's coming, the sense of expectancy should reach new heights. As the problem crystallizes, the speeches should become more hurried and the action more violent until the crowning dramatic surprise completes the story. Then, the curtain should be lowered slowly.

NOTES

a Currier and Ives print—a picture by the American lithographers and print publishers who depicted events and scenes of nineteenth century American life. Nathaniel Currier (1813-88) founded the firm in 1835, and the artist J. Merritt Ives joined him in 1850.
chromos—pictures that are printed in colours
spring freshets—spring floods caused by rain or melting snow

QUESTIONS

A

1. Explain the title.
2. Why does Ma refuse to move from her home on the banks of the Big Pebbly?
3. What premonition does she have?
4. How does the author dramatically give background information about Harry Holloway's past life?
5. Outline Tom's methods to prevent Ma from knowing the truth about her criminal son.

6. Account for Harry's returning home.
7. Tell how Tom learned that the fugitive would kill if necessary.
8. Find and read aloud the speech indicating that it was natural for Harry to use the window as a means of escape.
9. In what way is Tom "an accessory to murder"?

General

10. Write a plot summary of this play.

B

1. Why does the playwright include a detailed description of each character?
2. Discuss to what extent the dialect contributes to the success of the play.
3. In what ways is Ma's comparison of Harry to the Old River apt?
4. Account for Tom's refusal to obey the sheriff's command to shoot the convict.
5. Find two references for each of the following traits that Harry exhibits: cruelty, hypocrisy, and selfishness.
6. Read aloud the speech wherein Tom gives the escaping Harry one last chance to rectify matters legally. Why is it essential for the dramatist to include this speech?
7. One of the highest points of suspense in the play occurs when Tom cries out, "Ma! Ma, I had to do it!" Try to describe accurately what you thought and felt at this moment during your first reading of the play.
8. Select the climax of the play.

9. Enumerate the various factors that make the climax of this play particularly powerful.

General

10. Pretend that one of you is a casting director holding an audition for the rôles of the Holloway brothers. Having

described each character in detail, let several volunteers read the parts of Tom and Harry from the passage beginning "Hello, Tom!" and ending with "Well, I've got to be going!" Remind the actors to speak clearly and loudly. Award the two parts to the actors who most successfully create the characterizations from their readings.

C

1. Suggest as many reasons as possible for the author's confining Ma Holloway to a wheel chair.
2. Compare Harry and Tom with regard to (a) age, (b) appearance, (c) diction, and (d) manner.
3. Show how the fugitive's actions while he is alone on stage are calculated to command audience attention.
4. Why does Robert Arthur stress that Harry was always Ma's favourite son?
5. A surprise ending must seem credible. What clues does the sheriff give early in the play that enable us to accept the shocking conclusion?
6. Tom starts to warn Harry saying, "But the river—". Discuss how your picture of Tom would have been altered had these three words been omitted.
7. In any drama there are moments of dramatic pausing such as the stage directions of this play demand— "Tom stands for a long moment, staring at the empty window. He does not move until the sheriff emerges and comes over to him." Describe the audience's reaction to this example of the pausing device.
8. How did Harry's visit solve the problems of the Holloways?
9. Notice that the sheriff repeats Ma's exact words— "undercut right up to the house." Justify the repetition.

General

10. Pretend that in your capacity as drama critic for a local newspaper you have just seen a presentation of *Moon-Up*. Write a review of the play.

The Old Lady Shows Her Medals

SIR JAMES MATTHEW BARRIE (1860-1937), the novelist and dramatist, was born in Kirriemuir, Forfarshire, Scotland. During his attendance at Dumfries Academy, his early literary efforts included accounts of cricket matches and letters requesting longer vacations from school. There, he also wrote his first play *Bandelero the Bandit*. Later, he attended the University of Edinburgh, where he gained honours in English Literature and took his M.A. After graduation, he wrote for a Nottingham newspaper, and in 1885 he began writing sketches for *The British Weekly*. With his novel *The Little Minister* (1891), he was hailed as a first-rate novelist. His novels, written in the 1890's, treat Scottish parochial life in a humorous manner. From 1900-1920, he concentrated his creative writing powers on plays and was so successful that he is known today primarily as a playwright. Some of his famous plays are *The Admirable Crichton* (1902), *Peter Pan* (1904), *What Every Woman Knows* (1908), *Dear Brutus* (1917), and *Shall We Join the Ladies* (1922).

Two of the many important honours bestowed upon him were knighthood in 1913 and the degree of Doctor of Letters (University of Edinburgh) in 1922. Although he was world famous and wealthy, he lived modestly in a London flat till his death in 1937.

SUGGESTIONS FOR PRODUCING THE PLAY

The Old Lady Shows Her Medals is perhaps the most touching and amusing one-act play ever written. The plot thread is simple: a lonely, old Scottish charwoman pretends that she has a soldier son, and to her joyful surprise, he adopts her as his mother. Though the plot is somewhat contrived, the characterization and dialogue are so convincing that the audience is not aware of the basic inadequacy of the situation.

Some critics have objected to Barrie's whimsical sentimentality, but this is a personal judgment rather than a literary one. In terms of sincerity, tenderness, and humour, his characters are perfectly shaded. His sensitive, mildly satiric pictures of simple, ordinary people are unsurpassed in the world of drama. Snobbishness, we see, prevails amongst the London charwomen. Three of them, including the hostess, are called "charwoman and" which signifies that they do caretaking as well if necessary. This distinction raises their social class because their names are entered in a registry book; and they parade their rank in front of Mrs. Haggerty, who is just a charwoman and nothing else. Such injustice could be used as material for a powerful diatribe against class distinction, but Barrie

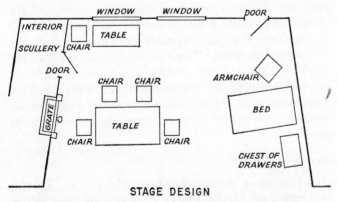

STAGE DESIGN

THE OLD LADY SHOWS HER MEDALS

merely touches on it delicately and causes us to laugh at the foolishness of human nature. We do more than laugh, however. When we encounter Mrs. Dowey's intense pride in her one room "with bed and bath," the ladies' hungry interest in women of fashion, their pathetically ignorant talk of war and War Savings Certificates, and the kindness of every character in the play, we are deeply moved. What keeps the entire play from becoming maudlin, though, is the essential human dignity each person possesses. Barrie may make us feel genuine concern for the people he creates, but he never lets us pity them. Each has her own niche and is relatively content with her lot in life.

Since this play was meant to be acted as well as read, the author's detailed comments provide valuable hints about presentation. There are, however, a few cautions to note. The accents required prove troublesome to some amateurs; therefore, it is wise to arrange many rehearsals. It is wise, too, to strive for the high quality of acting demanded by this play: weakness in Dowey's farewell scene and exaggerated playing by the charwomen can ruin the whole effect. Fortunately, though, the rapid development of the plot, the brilliant speeches, the amusing satire, and the subtle revelation of character provide so many wonderful moments that the audience readily forgives minor flaws in a group's presentation. Therefore, do not be afraid of the play! Its success will demand concentrated effort on everyone's part for a considerable length of time, but the play contains all the necessary directions, details of set design, and wonderfully warm people that a good script needs.

NOTES

charwoman—a woman hired usually by the day for housework or domestic tasks in institutions and offices
scullery—back kitchen

deal table—a table made of pinewood or fir planks

winkles—edible sea snails

the hob—that projection in a fireplace on which things are placed to maintain warmth

Salonikkey—Salonica, Salonika (săl ŏ ni′ kȧ), or Saloniki (săl ŏ nē′ kē) is the second largest Greek city. It is now called Thessalonike or Thessaloniki, the capital of Greek Macedonia on the Gulf of Salonica. No wonder the ladies in the play are confused by the various pronunciations and names. During World War I, an Allied force landed here for a peaceful blockade of Greece (1915).

cheek effect—Mrs. Tully means chic or stylish.

The Black Watch—The Black Watch regiment was originally organized by the British army in 1729 to keep peace in the Scottish Highlands. Unlike the British regulars, who wore scarlet breeches and coats, the Black Watch soldiers wore kilts and tartans of dark colours. When they were absorbed into the regular army as the 42nd regiment under the Earl of Crawford in 1737, the troops were allowed to retain their original uniform and name, although officially they are called "The Royal Highlanders."

The Buffs—a regimental nickname for The Royal East Kent Regiment, who take their name from the colour of their equipment. First raised in 1572, they were not properly constituted till 1664. Because of long service in Holland in the 17th century, they were originally called The Holland Regiment.

the Front—scene of actual fighting, the foremost line or part of an army

Blighty—army slang for England or the homeland. The expression came into popular use during World War I, but was used long before by soldiers who had served in India.

the covey—the company

limmer—immoral woman

drummles on like a Scotch burn—rumbles on like a Scottish brook

Oh havers!—Oh, nonsense!

a skite—a spree

a randy-dandy—a gay frolic

Carter, glazier, orra man—A carter is a man who drives a cart; a glazier is one who glazes windows; an orra man is a farm labourer who does odd jobs.

Tuylleries—Dowey means the Tuileries, a former palace in Paris so named because of the tile-yards (tuileries) once on the site. Planned by Catherine de' Medici in 1564, it stood between the Louvre and the Place de la Concorde. In 1871, a mob burned it down, but the gardens remain today as a beautiful public open space.

the Louvre—once the royal palace of the French kings in Paris. Since the French Revolution, most of the Louvre has been used as a national museum and art gallery.

a shake-down—straw or blankets on a floor as a bed

the dodge—the trick

a cove—a slang expression meaning fellow

merino—a garment made of fine woollen yarn from the merino sheep

chiffon—a soft, silky, thin, gauze-like material

kit—soldier's knapsack

astrakhan coat—made from the skin of young lambs with wool-like fur obtained from Astrakhan, Russia

You bricks!—slang expression meaning kind, generous people

bonny—comely

QUESTIONS

A

Scene 1

1. Who are Mrs. Dowey's guests?
2. What aspects of the tea party are humorous?

3. State the news that the Reverend Mr. Wilkinson brings.
4. How does Mrs. Dowey react to this information?
5. Describe Kenneth Dowey.
6. Why did he come to see Mrs. Dowey?
7. In explaining Mrs. Dowey's duplicity in connection with Kenneth, give her motives for such deceit.

Scene 2

8. Account for the presence of the charwomen in Mrs. Dowey's room as this scene opens.

Scene 3

9. Find several expressions in the stage directions that suggest Kenneth Dowey is now dead.

General

10. From your recent reading, find a passage of good dialogue that parallels *The Old Lady Shows Her Medals* in the sense that a deceitful person is on the point of being found out. Discuss the merits of the selections.

B

Scene 1

1. Select the words in the opening set description that indicate the poverty of Mrs. Dowey.
2. Notice that even the stage directions are often gently comic. Find five such examples that prove that this play was meant to be read as well as acted.
3. Discuss why the charwomen strongly resent any woman who does not have a male relative at war.
4. Justify Barrie's using the contrived meeting between Mr. Wilkinson and Kenneth Dowey, and the coincidence of the latter's name being the same as Mrs. Dowey's pretended son.
5. Under what condition does Kenneth agree to stay with the old lady?
6. Why does the playwright present the soldier as brusque and callous rather than openly sympathetic?

Scene 2

7. How is the snobbishness of the women emphasized?
8. Describe in detail the farewell scene between Kenneth and Mrs. Dowey.

Scene 3

9. Why would the background music be effective here?

General

10. Present Scene 2 of *The Old Lady Shows Her Medals* as a radio play; if possible, secure a tape recorder and later play back your effort. Be wary of muffled speeches, unrealistic sound effects, and meaningless pauses that will detract from the effectiveness of your production.

C

Scene 1

1. Why is Mrs. Haggerty unpopular with the other ladies?
2. Prove that each of the guests is intensely proud.
3. "Barrie is a master satirist." Show the truth of this statement by using detailed references to the behaviour of the women at the tea party.
4. (*a*) Outline the interview between Kenneth and Mrs. Dowey.
   (*b*) What is pathetic about this meeting?
   (*c*) What is humorous about it?
5. Discuss why Mrs. Dowey now destroys her cherished letters.

Scene 2

6. Act out the unit wherein the ladies talk about war as they wait for the arrival of Mrs. Dowey and her son. What is there that is comically pathetic about this passage?
7. Account for the pleasure that the other ladies experience by observing and commenting on Mrs. Dowey's relationship with Kenneth.

8. If you were directing the play, what acting instructions would you give the players who participate in the farewell unit of action.

Scene 3

9. Although no dialogue is present in this scene, it provides perhaps the most moving moments in the play. Show how the author has assured the success of the play's ending.

General

10. Create from heavy cardboard a small stage of the set described at the beginning of this play. Include furniture and properties to provide an authentic model of the setting required for the final production. This practice may be performed in groups.